12.00

Doolally

Edited by David Gill

Every sport pretends to be a literature, but people don't believe it of any sport but their own

Alistair Cooke

Football is poetry – and anyone who doesn't believe that has nothing interesting to say about football – or poetry.

The Armchair Philosopher

PDG Books 2005

Doolally is published by PDG Books Ltd

Registered company number 5334818
www.pdgbooks.com

ISBN 1-905519-00-1 / 978-1-905519-00-2

Cover design by Megan Hawes
Willie Whistle illustration by Jem Lee

Printed by The Charlesworth Group

Contents

Foreword

Doolally: Slang. out of one's mind; crazy; mentally deranged or feeble minded; transported with excitement or pleasure. [originally military slang Doolally Tap, from Deolali, a town near Mumbai, the location of a military sanatorium, + tap, Urdu 'fever'].

Feck: Northern and Scots dialects. 1. one of the stomachs of ruminants [Paunch, Read & Feck]. 2. worth; value. 3. vigour, power. [cf. feckless, worthless; ineffective; feeble; destitute of vigour, energy or capacity; weak, helpless].

Feckful: efficient; vigorous; powerful

Feckwit: value wit; wit-power.

Feck off: literally, worth off: alternatively, get your worthless arse out of town: alt. "You're on a free transfer."

Feckin doolally: lit. valuing doolally: alt. valuing madness.

I've always been head-spinningly heart-wrenchingly gut-churningly ball-breakingly toe-curlingly mad about football. I love the game. Played properly, it's a thing of beauty and a force for good.

I've supported my beloved Leeds United and of course The Republic of Ireland since I can remember. As a kid back in Ireland I had sew-on Leeds patches on my coat and trousers. I also sported a lovely Leeds ring on my finger. Just seeing the word "Leeds" on motorway signs gets me excited to this day.

If the truth be known, though, I have a mental stumbling block when it comes to writing about Leeds, struggling to write anything uplifting. I've tried to start something on a few occasions but within minutes find myself weeping uncontrollably.

I've got to hand it to these guys for what they've come up with. They're definitely DOOLALLY!

Love and best wishes to all the readers and writers of this book!

Ardal O'Hanlon,
August 2005

Psycho Analysis

"Football's always easier when you've got the ball."

Kevin Keegan

The Psychiatrists

by Graeme Garvey

'Why Leeds?'

'*Why breathe?*' he said, and it seemed like he really meant it.

'So, following Leeds United is as important to you as life itself?'

'Easily, pal! - erm, Dr Ronson.'

It confirmed all of the psychiatrist's suspicions. Jim Taylor was mad – relaxed, calm, but completely barmy and, although the question had been answered with a happy shrug, that had only served to depress him. The psychiatrist that was, not Jim. Dispassionate professional he might be, yet he still felt sorry for his client because his job was on the line. Jim's that was, not the psychiatrist's. Taylor's very future depended on the report that his employers had requested and yet he appeared to be totally unconcerned. Seeing Ronson's worried look, Jim attempted to cheer him up.

'I know you're trying to help me, Dr Ronson, but that's just how I feel. Leeds United mean everything to me.'

Despite the fact his client had an illness, clearly shown by this total infatuation with a football club, the psychiatrist couldn't avoid liking him. He had warmed to him over their regular counselling sessions over that spring and early summer. It was sickening, anyway, having to do a clinical report for employers who had tired of their employee's obsession. Why didn't they just come straight out and fire the unfortunate Jim? Why did they have to hide behind his report? At times like this, he hated his job.

From his office door, he bade Taylor goodbye, agreeing they would meet once the report was completed and then he returned to his desk. Although it was midsummer now, Ronson's mood was more in sync with a gloomy January. His drab office was on the top floor of the teaching hospital near Leeds City Centre. Though he rarely bothered to look out, all that could be seen from his window was a car park and acres more of the hospital's concrete and glass, except for a partial view of the cityscape through a small gap which Taylor had once made some odd comments about. He easily resisted the urge to take in the vista and sank down in his swivel chair to review the whole case. Jim was fruitcake nuts on Leeds United, of that he was certain, even if he might have to express it a little more tactfully in his final report. He opened his file and began reading;

```
Draft clinical report on James T. Taylor:-

Client details - James Terence Taylor, born
8th December 1968.
Married to - Lynn.
Father of two - Jane 14, Allan 12.
Employment - Computer technician. In current
job at Leodis Computer Manufacturers for
seven years.
Behavioural patterns - Superficially, seems
reasonably normal, well-adjusted but displays
classic underlying symptoms of delusional
behaviour, most clearly shown by his
obsessional attitude towards football in
general and Leeds United in particular.
```

He was more used to dealing with people who thought they were Napoleon. Most of his cases flowed along sadly predictable lines. He had been stumped, though, by this fellow's blithe complacency. So, having been at a total loss about what to write, he had fallen back on the old tactic of dividing his report into five sections. Somebody, sometime, somewhere or other, had said something about stuff happening in fives. True or not, the tactic normally impressed, especially when it came wrapped in a plush binder. He hoped that using the 5-Part trick would suggest he had spotted a pattern to Taylor's eccentric behaviour. He knew it was nonsense, really. All they wanted was an excuse to sack the man. Allowing Jim to condemn himself from his own mouth, Ronson would base the report on his comments, neatly editing out most of his own words. The headings were taken from some of Taylor's more outlandish claims:

Part 1, 'I play for Leeds United.'

Part 2, 'If I had to manage Leeds.'

Part 3, 'Why did the police arrest ME?'

Part 4, 'It's good to hate Man U.'

Part 5, 'My boss has almost got used to me now.'

I play for Leeds United

The psychiatrist feared that the full report would provide all the evidence that the employers needed. It hadn't boded well from the outset, right from when Mr Taylor, or Jim as he had come to regard him, had said he believed he actually played for Leeds United. Part 1 had it all. In it, Jim freely admitted that he had never been any good as a football player himself, yet came out with the incredible claim that he genuinely felt he was one of the team. As he reached for the tape, inserted it in the machine and pressed "play", Ronson was transported by it back to their first recorded conversation.

'Leeds need me,' Jim had said. 'but I always take care of my own kit. Naturally, it's a white shirt for home games and either yellow or blue if we are on our travels. I play every ball, make every tackle with the lads.'

The psychiatrist then asked him if he thought he was the team's manager.

Jim ridiculed that, 'What do you think I am, mad? Course not. I'm a player. Every fan is. I have to try like crazy some games and I'm usually completely knackered by the end. Even fans who went in the "Glory, Glory" years, when Leeds were the best team around, say they had to try really hard. Imagine you're on the Kop, or in the Family Stand, there's only minutes to go and Leeds get a corner. If we score from it, you don't reckon the ball goes in just by itself do you?'

Deeply suspicious that he was being sent up by Taylor but with his curiosity raised, Dr Ronson put a question to him.

'If that is true, then why don't Leeds score all the time?'

'Simple.' came the reply. Taylor appeared to feel his answer was self-evident. Noting only a look of puzzlement from his interrogator, he continued, 'It's kept out by all the opposition fans trying their clacks off for them!'

Ronson said nothing. It had made him think. After a pause he went on, 'Tell me. I thought you didn't go to every match any more.'

'Sadly, no,' Jim confided with a slight hint of shame, 'I have to give most away matches a miss nowadays, what with the kids and all that. *"Shop-ping all to-geth-er!"*.'

He started to sing, slightly varying the Leeds anthem to fit his changed circumstances, until he saw the rising panic in the psychiatrist's face and subsided into silence.

'If you don't attend every match, you can't possibly be playing for Leeds, then can you?'

'Of course I can, and I do. You don't have to actually go to games, to play for Leeds…although it does help.'

'Pray explain.' said a bemused Ronson.

Jim did explain, patiently, in a kindly way. He had formed a liking for the man who was being paid to psychoanalyse him, despite his pitiful ignorance of football's mysterious workings.

'If I watch it on telly, it's quite easy. I try to will the ball in when we attack and help the lads tackle when we defend.'

'Not forgetting midfield.' the psychiatrist added helpfully, half pleased with his growing football knowledge and half ashamed to be joining in the delusion.

'Not forgetting midfield.' Jim concurred, happy with that thoughtful contribution. He would make a Leeds fan of Ronson yet.

'So, by "playing for Leeds" you basically mean you are willing them on?'

'Oh no, it's much more than that. You're trying to help each player in turn, running with him, tackling and jumping with him. It's exhausting.'

Exhausted by all this weird and wonderful philosophy, the psychiatrist hit the pause button, stopping to reflect before again pressing play. He had come to one of the most astonishing bits and wanted to really concentrate.

'Midfield has been a bit of a problem for a while, since you mention it. I feel too often like we're being overrun. Sometimes I've had to resort to throwing things at the telly to put the opposition off. It's not cheating, really, more gamesmanship.'

'Throwing things?'

'Yeh, mostly darts with rubber suckers but I've used table tennis balls occasionally when I've wanted to just catch 'em a glancing blow. We call it a Professional Foul. And our Allan's been a godsend. Ever since he could crawl, he's been fetching them back for me to fire again.'

'And has all this helped your team to play better?'

'Oh yes. Definitely. Lots.'

After that comment, Ronson, changing tack, had returned to how Taylor claimed to be able to play for Leeds at times when he didn't even go the game. He felt that if his client could just settle for supporting his team he might yet get him off the hook but the poor man was adamant what he did made a difference to his team's performance, whether at the game or not. Jim, ingeniously, had elaborate systems worked out when forced to miss seeing the game. If he had to listen to the match on local radio, he sat in his favourite chair and then no one could speak to him unless Leeds scored. He would rock backwards and forwards, shouting regular abuse at the commentators for falsely getting up his hopes.

When the commentators irritated him too much, he followed the game on teletext. Then, Jim invented scenarios based around the skeletal facts that popped up when a goal was scored or a player sent off. He would launch daring attacks, frantically repel opposition raids, struggle for midfield dominance. That was why he usually ended up completely knackered, apparently.

'Tell me more about teletext.' Ronson said. He wasn't really trying to trap Jim at this point, his genuine interest had been won.

The invitation was picked up immediately by Taylor. 'It's not bad, honestly.' he replied. 'Ok, it's not like being there but you can definitely play for Leeds on teletext. What I like about it is how little it interferes, just giving the latest score and who's been sent off. It leaves you plenty of room to fill in all the details. For example, when we get a goal, it names the scorer, so you can create the move leading up to it, in your head. Likewise, if we let a goal in, you can imagine whose fault it was and give 'em a good bollocking. Then you can check how close you were on telly later on. You're usually not far wrong.'

'Quite.' his psychiatrist said, completely mystified. This man's job was in jeopardy but he was far more interested in fantasising. 'Tell me now about what happens if you have to go out when a match is on?' he asked. Ronson could detect, on playback, the growing fascination in his own voice.

'If I go out? That's murder. It doesn't happen often – the wife's very good you know, but if it does, I have to play the whole game in my head.'

'You play the whole game in your head?'

'Yep, that's right.'

Jim, ever inventive, spent all of his time at the garden centre/ shoe shop/ supermarket trying to make space for himself, disengaging from would-be tacklers and leaving himself room for a free header.

Ronson, not being a football fan, was still struggling to come to terms with all this nonsense as he pressed the stop button but there was a weird attraction to the grotesque imaginings of his client.

To the accusation, then, that Jim Taylor really believed he played for Leeds United, the only plea was guilty. He didn't actually kick the ball but was convinced he did make a difference to the outcome of a match. There could be no defence then, when the accused boasted of it. It just seemed so unfair that such enthusiasm, even if misplaced, was going to cost him his job.

If I had to manage Leeds

He noticed that cars had already filled almost every grid in the regimented bays beside the teaching hospital. Forehead pressed against the glass, Dr Michael Ronson had had a good night, too good. Born on June 6th, he had been out for drinks with some colleagues to celebrate his birthday and was now paying for it. D-Day for him had meant Drinks Day. Until that moment his eyes had been tight shut. He had only opened them to check if he was still alive. He was trying, most of all, to blot out the headcrushing effects of far too much vodka. Suddenly, an aged Vauxhall Astra screamed into the car park. It swung into a narrow space, shunned by all others, as if the driver had been practising that manoeuvre all his life. The engine died. Ronson continued looking down and then nothing happened for a considerable time. The only sound to disturb the silence was the crash of forty thousand anvils being struck inside his brain. His instinct told him who the driver was and it told him that person had found himself too tightly parked for the room to get out comfortably. His instinct had not lied. Eventually a door edged open and a large-sized man squeezed out. Jim Taylor was on his way.

Composing himself to interview his job-doomed victim, the psychiatrist suddenly felt compromised. Here was a man who he had been literally looking down on, who was large and out of condition, and yet, in a way, he envied him for his feckless happiness. For the first time, he was beginning to wonder if Taylor was quite as pathetic as he'd thought.

He called to mind, carefully, so as not to anger the vodka gods, the letter from Jim's boss at Leodis Computer Manufacturers. Using the minimum of movement necessary to reach into Taylor's file, he scanned its contents to remind himself of why they wanted him sacked.

Dr Ronson,

We wish to make use of your services to produce a report on the mental stability of one of our employees, Mr James T Taylor. The management feel there are strong grounds to support the view that his obsession and infatuation with Leeds United Football Club has reduced his work output to such an extent that it has rendered him a liability at LCM.

We note that our company and your institution have enjoyed a harmonious working relationship for several years now and are confident a person of your professional reputation and competence will be able to furnish us with the necessary evidence to allow us to proceed with downsizing our workforce by one. We look forward with confidence to continuing our sponsorship, despite the more difficult economic times we are living through.

With full trust in your ability to produce a report along the suggested lines, we will leave it in your capable hands. Below are just a few of the many examples of Taylor's peculiar behaviour at LCM.

Yours sincerely, Simon Jenkins, Systems Manager, LCM.

Below that slimy letter, and gone over with a fluorescent green marker pen to make the oddness appear as odd as possible were the following examples of his "peculiar behaviour":

- Placing notices in the Leodis company car park banning all red cars.

- Making a written request that company stationery be changed from cream to white with blue and yellow embossing, and a yellow smiley face.

- Putting in monthly written requests for the company to change its name because 'Manufacturers' begins with four offensive letters.

- Requesting "compassionate leave" the day after Leeds were relegated.

- Keeping a computer permanently open on the Leeds United website "in case of emergencies".

By the time Taylor had made it into the room, with his customary breeziness, the whingeing letter had been ever so gently returned to its rightful place in the darkness of his drawer. Bravely crunching on some aspirins, Ronson turned towards his client who was evidently ready to talk turkey.

'You don't know what it's like, having to put up with all that crap. We've had some lousy managers.'

'Do you mean at work?'

'Nah. Well, when you come to mention it, there too. But I meant at Leeds United.'

The psychiatrist had been hoping to get Jim Taylor to address his work problems but the client was slippery as an eel when it came to that. He dragged everything back, quick as a flash, to the fantasy world where he had a major part to play in the fortunes of his beloved football team. Classic self-delusion, of course, Ronson reflected, but he had to stay strong mentally because he found himself being drawn in to the imaginative world Jim painted.

'Tell me about "all that crap".'

'Well what bugs me is that these guys think they can run a football team when it's obvious to everyone that the players just please themselves.'

'By "these guys" you mean football managers?' Dr Ronson offered.

'Spot on, matey.' a beaming Jim said with just enough charm to avoid insult. 'Top players are so wealthy these days, I reckon that if they don't fancy doing something, it doesn't get done. They don't even have to say anything. Their agents do all that. Hey, I'm just thinking, Dr Ronson. You're kind of like my agent, aren't you?'

The psychiatrist's heart hurt nearly as much as his brain. The poor, misguided man simply refused to accept how tough a spot he really was in.

Peace, though, was gradually returning to Ronson's head. There could be no more than fifteen thousand anvils still being hammered.

Tops. As far as he could tell, in accompaniment with his own Anvil Chorus, the client was a humming a tune he, Jim, very much favoured and to which he, Ronson, was growing familiar.

At the weekend, it transpired, the Leeds manager had done something to incur Jim's wrath. He had either signed someone Taylor did not approve of, or sold someone he did approve of, or possibly both. The psychiatrist couldn't fathom it at all. Anyway, it looked like another person who did not actually play for Leeds United believed he could influence what happened on the field of play. Whoever this manager was, and the name meant nothing to him, Ronson feared there was a growing prospect of having to write another report on yet another deluded client.

Once into his stride, Jim explained in undreamed of detail about what he would do as boss of the team, about how he would organise the "back four", what he would do with free kicks and when he would use tactical substitutes. What he became most animated about was how things could go so wrong during a game that it seemed impossible to believe the players had ever even met each other before, let alone spent months together practising.

'If I had to manage Leeds, at least they'd play like a team.'

'You don't like your job do you, Mr Taylor?'

'No.'

Why did the police arrest ME?

'Do you ever feel aggressive at a football match, Mr Taylor?'

'Call me Jim, will you? I feel funny with all of this Mr Taylor stuff.'

'Very well. Do you ever feel aggressive at a football match, Jim?'

'I suppose so, kind of, sometimes, but I wouldn't harm a fly me, really.'

'Have you had any fights?'

'Not as such. As you can see, I'm a fairly big lad, so I don't get pushed around too often.'

'Then, if you don't mind me asking, Jim, how did you come to be arrested?'

'That's exactly what I want to know. Why did the police arrest ME?'

As Dr Ronson reviewed the tape in preparing this section of his report, he recalled it had been intended to investigate whether his client had any deep-seated feelings of frustration and aggression. What Jim had just said seemed to suggest the possibility of adding a persecution complex to the list. He had invited Taylor to speak freely.

'What a stupid idea anyway, allowing a vital promotion match to go ahead on a bank holiday in a seaside resort like Bournemouth. It was asking for trouble and trouble's just what I got! Usually, my size has kept me out of harm but, every so often, the opposite happens and it makes me a target.'

Whilst he was speaking, Jim was standing by the window in the office, looking out. When invited to sit down and talk about his arrest, he declined. Ronson was keen for him to sit before he spoke on such an emotional subject. The textbooks said not to have a client stand up when dealing with anger, in case it made him over-aggressive.

'Please do sit down, Jim, and tell me what happened.'

'Ok,' Taylor said, 'but, I don't know if you've noticed. Looking out of your window, if you stand just here, you can see a bit of the city centre.'

'I suppose you can.' the psychiatrist replied without enthusiasm. He couldn't get the point of all this.

Taylor gleefully proclaimed, 'Yeah and from there it's nobbut a stride to Elland Road.' before sitting down to tell his tale of seaside woe.

'Although Leeds fans had a reputation for being nutters in them days, I reckon it was as much the League's fault but nobody is allowed to blame them are they? Normally, I'm ok when there's bother, as I've said, since I'm tall, and, to use Lynn's phrase, "well-rounded".

'We'd been cooped up in a smeggy coach all the way from Leeds. No one told me how far it was to the south coast. And England's supposed to be small. It took us ages. Any road, we finally arrived, got parked and made for the chip shop. Food, then pints, then the match. That was the plan, at least.

'As we made our way down towards the sea front scoffing us dinners, this huge mob of Bournemouth fans appeared at the end of the street. There were about twenty of us and we just stood our ground as they approached. One of their lot started throwing punches but, you've got to remember, most of us had trays of fish and chips in our hands. Not exactly useful weapons. So pretty soon it wasn't just the fish that was battered. I can remember a load of their fans, mostly teenagers, leaping up on me as I'm trying to protect my dinner. They weren't going to have my grub, so I sort of spun round a few times and most of them fell off. Just then, the Boys in Blue arrived. Thank goodness, I thought, and then I realised that the scuffers thought it was me throwing my weight about. All they'd seen was flying Bournemouth fans. There were bodies and chips everywhere. They grabbed hold of me and, I'm not making this up, one of them really said, "You're nicked."

'All that, just because I was tall and stood out. I lost my fish and chips and I missed the match and the party after. I could hear all the cheering from the cells. Honest, Dr Ronson, I was the victim.'

Ronson made a connection.

'Do you accept there is a possibility your bosses might be about to make a victim of you now?'

Jim looked at him with just a hint of uncertainty before replying.

'It is a bit like at work, actually. Do you reckon they are after me there 'cos I'm the tallest? Anyway, I don't reckon they're really, really after me. I think it's just talk. But I didn't get out of nick till the following morning, plus a fine just for trying to save my chips.'

Sitting there in all his bulk, puzzled and still hurt by this ancient injustice, Taylor looked to the psychiatrist like a gentle giant and he concluded that Jim did not display particular signs of aggression. From the evidence, nor did he have a persecution complex. Quite the reverse, in fact. He did not even realise when he was being persecuted. Dr Ronson went over to his bookshelf to find a complex fitting that definition.

It's good to hate Man U

Three of the five parts to his report were now in place, the fourth was nearing completion and, the further he progressed, the more unhappy he became with the whole business. On a fine evening in mid July, Dr Michael Ronson queued in traffic on his way home from work. His preoccupation with staring at the rear end of a chunky four by four was rudely interrupted by his phone chiming a cheesy rendition of the theme from *Love Story*. It was his girlfriend Clarissa. He loved Clarrisa. Indeed he worshipped the ground on which she trod but…no, he mustn't be disloyal, even in his thoughts. Oh, all right, she did witter on a bit. And she did tend to tell him off a little too readily. But that was all, well, almost all…

It was a chirpy, friendly chat. Lots of "love yous" flew back and forth but the outcome was that he hadn't forgotten the anchovies had he? He had reassuringly replied that of course he hadn't and then immediately left the queue in search of anchovy. *Tescos* was his only chance at such short notice. Clarissa was so experimental, leastways, she was in the kitchen.

Hoping and praying they had some what-do-you-call-its, he picked up a hand basket and he set off in hot pursuit of his quarry. He would probably have found it or them quite quickly if he hadn't already forgotten what he was meant to buy. He was so preoccupied these days. All he was confident of by now was that it began with "a" and was probably either some sort of fish or vegetable. Artichoke? Anchovy? Aubergine? Asparagus? He wandered the aisles, slowly becoming more desperate, searching for inspiration, hoping that seeing the correct "a" would trigger his memory until suddenly, and by sheer chance, he struck gold. In triumph, he called out, 'Anchovies!' before remembering he was in a public place. Luckily no one seemed to have noted his call of greeting and he was just reaching for a tin when he heard voices to his left that froze his outstretched arm a mere inch from its target.

'Allan, Jane, what was it your dad wanted?'

'Scampi.' said the girl.

'Sure?' asked the woman, who was clearly their mother.

'Oh yes. Definitely. Lots.' said the boy who was even more clearly Allan.

Ronson felt he had struck gold a second time. Remembering to grab the anchovies, he gazed in fascination as Jim Taylor's family ambled away. Jim's wife, Lynn it must be, was a good-looking woman. Her children were bonny, too, and Allan was already tall, like his dad. What a realisation had dawned on him, though. Jim wasn't a client, he was a living, breathing human being who fully existed outside of the psychiatrist's office. Names on a list; Lynn, Jane, Allan, had come to life.

Entranced, he could not help but follow the Taylors a little way. He was the professional, building background on his client. That was all. From a distance, he pursued them as far as the checkouts.

Allan wore what was obviously a football shirt, a blue one with some sort of company name emblazoned on the front. Jane wore one, too, only hers was yellow. He had to concede that Lynn looked very good in her white one.

He felt a sudden inexplicable impulse to buy a bottle of Scots whisky, *Whyte and Mackay* being perhaps his favoured choice and then he remembered himself and he then also remembered Clarissa. With only one item to pay for, he made for the express till, committing the Taylor family to memory.

Returning next day to the fourth part of his report, he was still as confused as ever about all the football talk but he was beginning to view the whole thing rather differently. He was feeling less and less in a position to pity "poor" Jim.

'Lynn's a cracker, you know.'

Taylor's comment burst out brightly from the recorder, revealing a man who might be having big problems holding on to his job but who was loving and evidently loved. Not for the first time but now much more sharply, Ronson had to hold back a real tinge of envy.

'Sometimes I think she's more potty on Leeds than I am. Ever since we met at the Supporters' Club annual bash, I knew she was the right one for me. Oh yes, she looks more level-headed to other people but, do you know, she and her mum are forever sending each other text messages about the club. We're talking hundreds here.'

'What's wrong with that?'

'Nowt. But they don't say owt. They say daft stuff like the reserve team goalie's got a cold.'

This had been way too much for the psychiatrist to take in at the time of interview. He had desperately sought an explanation for it all. Ever since meeting James Terence Taylor, Michael Ronson had become alert to the fact that there was so much he didn't know. He needed to learn a whole new language to understand Jim's world. He was a fast learner, though and had asked his client to elucidate.

Jim managed to convince him that there was no subject too trivial for mother and daughter to text one another about. To the psychiatrist, it was not just a new language, it was all like visiting a foreign country. He moved the conversation on to other family members, Taylor's children, Allan and Jane. Jane was named after her grandma but when the son was born, a family tradition was resumed. Allan had been named after Leeds hero Allan "Sniffer" Clarke whose major claim to fame, it appeared, was putting the ball in the Arsenal net when Leeds won the FA Cup.

'Same for me, really.' Taylor said. Yet another puzzled Ronson look led to an explanation. 'Notice when I was born, December 1968 but notice more significantly when I was popped in by my rascally mum and dad!'

'Are we talking about your conception, here, Jim?'

'We sure are. The very night Leeds won the League Cup, 2nd March, 1968 to celebrate, like. And who scored the only goal that day? The great Terry Cooper of course. And what's my name?'

Something in the challenge of that last question half-prompted Dr Ronson to say 'Muhammad Ali?' He was too professional, so he made do with, 'James Terence Taylor.'

'Exactly. James after me dad and Terence for Terry Cooper.'

Jim glowed with pleasure.

Ronson pretended to write a note while he tried to absorb all this. "Terry Cooper" meant nothing to him but he knew by now that it meant a great deal to Jim. He had to be a footballer of some repute. Eventually he looked up and said, 'It is quite clear you love your family as well as Leeds United. Is there anyone you hate?'

That question can be relied on to secure a strong response. That was its intent. The psychiatrist, though, was surprised by how thoughtful Taylor became before answering.

'Father O'Donnell said it was wrong to say you hate someone when you really mean "strongly dislike, or can't stand, or that they make you sick". So I asked him about Man United and if I could say I hated them. At first he said positively not but then we had a bit of a talk. I reminded him their nickname was the Red Devils. He thought God wouldn't be very pleased with that nickname. I reminded him they were the richest club in the world. He tut-tutted and said something about camels and eyes of needles, rich men and heaven. It was a little confusing but the upshot of it seemed to be that money can't buy true happiness.

'I saw my chance and then reminded him how Man U buy all the best players and don't care a thing about anyone else. He said that was not at all Christian and he could see my point. I said, "So is it all right to hate Man U?" and he told me I should say I hate how corrupt Man U are. I agreed with him but it's harder to sing all that so when I'm at Elland Road I just shorten it to fit the line, "Stand up, if you hate Man U".'

'Very interesting,' Michael Ronson said, 'do you think, though,

25

you are perhaps looking to excuse how much you detest Manchester United by seeking for your priest's support?'

Jim Taylor was puzzled. 'Detest? I detest liver. I HATE Man U.'

'All right, then, hate Manchester United.'

'You might have a point, doc. Fr O'Donnell is a big Leeds fan, anyway. That's why I didn't ask Fr Wilson. He follows the Scum.'

'The Scum?'

'Man U. Scum. Scum floats on the top,' Jim said in explanation before continuing, 'and my boss, Simon Jenkins, supports them. He would, wouldn't he? I told Fr O'Donnell who said it was a shame and that we should pray for him. I said I prayed every day the boss would see the light and start to follow Leeds.'

'I hope you haven't told your boss this.' Dr Ronson said with genuine concern. He wondered if there were, potentially, even more grounds for dismissal. An employee whom the boss saw as lazy, incompetent and who was also praying for him! Perhaps not, but Jim's case looked more and more hopeless the more he found out.

My boss is almost getting used to me now

"With full trust in your ability to produce a report along the suggested lines."

Great. The cowards. Leodis Computer Manufacturers had resorted to pretty sly tactics to get rid of "that Leeds nutter on the fourth floor". It was true that the psychiatrist was no nearer working out what Jim Taylor actually did every day, even after months of meetings. Whenever he broached the subject, Jim's eyes glazed over. The most he ever got out of him was that at least he didn't make weapons of mass destruction. Ronson's best guess was that his client was on nodding terms with motherboards. He based this on the fleeting references Jim had occasionally made to such boards, but he didn't call them exactly that, always inserting an obscenity between "mother" and "board".

Ronson had never actually met anyone from LCM Ltd. He just had that name of Simon Jenkins, Systems Manager, from the letter. In truth, he had had no less than four subsequent letters from that same Simon Jenkins, asking for progress updates, to which he had replied each time saying progress was "ongoing". He reckoned not meeting face-to-face stopped them having to get their hands dirty by feeling directly involved. They would probably end up sacking Jim by email. The official reason was because Ronson was supposed to be impartial. He knew this was impossible since they sponsored his department, funding its research into the deepest corners of the mind. All they wanted back was a bit of what Ronson was meant to be producing now – a damning report.

'You know how you've got this report to write? Well it might not be too bad because I think my boss, Simon Jenkins, is getting used to me now.'

Those had been the parting words by the office door at the last psychiatrist/client meeting when the report was about to be written up and the scale of Jim's error couldn't fail to fill him with sadness. The deluded fool, he had thought, Taylor just hadn't a clue. His words had carried with them a pathetic sense of groundless optimism and, bless him, he had seemed more concerned for his psychiatrist than himself.

Remembering this tragic example of self-deception, Dr Ronson decided to review the whole case prior to completing his report. There was no denying he had grown to like Jim Taylor more and more as time had gone by. Yes, Jim was obsessed by Leeds United Football Club but somehow, magically, it had made him a better not worse person. He loved his family, he was overly enthusiastic towards Leeds but his aggressive posturing about the opposition was all bluff. Ronson suspected that his experience at Bournemouth, when he was arrested for violent behaviour, was probably an experience typical of many supporters: the real rogues always get away with it.

It had reached late July and he had been spinning out the process with his client for weeks, trying to put off the inevitable. The time had finally come, though, to submit his findings to LCM. He couldn't delay any longer. It ought to be easy, just confirm all of their suspicions and move on to the next case. He longed for the simplicity of only having to deal with Napoleons.

He knew Taylor was waiting outside as he was forcing himself to make the fateful decision. He could hear Jim humming to himself, untroubled as ever. Ronson had learned it was the Leeds club anthem that Jim was so fond of. Walking back over to his office window, he stood in the spot Taylor especially liked, with its cityscape view, between hospital buildings, that indirectly pointed towards Elland Road. He remembered seeing Jim's fine family shopping in *Tescos*. Then he made his decision.

He wouldn't go ahead with it, he couldn't go ahead with it. To hell with them, he was not going to be the instrument of a good man's dismissal, even if it meant him looking for a new employer himself, so be it. There were plenty more troubled minds out there.

When he invited Jim into the office, he did so with a feeling of relief and a newfound sense of daring. His breaking of the news to Jim, though, did not have quite the bombshell effect Ronson had anticipated. Taylor looked puzzled for a second or two, then a dawning understanding broke on his shapeless, amiable face.

'Thanks, pal,' he said, 'but you don't need to bother with that report anyway. They've sacked Jenkins and the new boss is a Leeds fan. Says we can forget it all.'

Dr Michael Ronson sat there, absolutely stunned, for a considerable while.

Jim, troubled by this torpor, looked on with concern but then brightened again and continued, 'And guess what? The season kicks off in three weeks. First match is at home. Fancy coming?'

Still bewildered, the trained psychiatrist looked straight at his patient. Bit by bit he began to take in the genuine sincerity of the man seated opposite. Jim was truly appreciative of the courageous gesture. This was his way of saying thanks. It hadn't been for nothing.

Slowly Ronson came back to his senses and then spoke with an honest timidity, 'Well…I've never been to a football match.'

'You kid?'

'No, I wasn't very good at it at school. Then I just drifted off to university and got too busy after that.'

'In that case, it's time you went. You'll love it.'

'…Ok…but what will Clariss…Oh, what the hell. Why not!'

Coda

It is a balmy afternoon in August. Thousands of bums lift off seats as the Whites attack. Chanting spreads like wildfire round the North East corner and along the Family Stand at Elland Road. Jim Taylor, large as life and breathing heavily to prove it, is singing lustily at the top of his voice. To his right are Lynn, Jane and Allan. To his left is a newcomer. He also stands, albeit a little unsurely, somewhat like a newborn lamb. There is just a hint of him mouthing the words to the Leeds anthem of "Marching on Together", a song he has virtually learned by osmosis from Jim's regular renditions of it in his waiting room. Dr Michael Ronson, hang-ups hung up in his office, is actually beginning to enjoy himself. Taylor gives him a big hug, singing discordantly in his ear, and the psychiatrist doesn't mind one bit.

Football is all very well as a game for rough girls, but is hardly suitable for delicate boys

Oscar Wilde

BEASTMOUSE

by Pat Wainwright

'Some t*** came to teach us about creative writing.'

That's how the story started.

Not this story. This story might have started when me dad started telling me about all those times Leeds got shafted in the 70s.

No, some t*** came to teach us about creative writing and told us to write something, anything. If we couldn't think of anything just write about today, like a diary.

So I wrote:

'Some t*** came to teach us about creative writing.'

He was prowling about and came up behind me and that was a bit risky cos I don't like people coming up behind me. He told me I'd better not write t***, I'd better use asterixes. I know what asterixes are, I got me GCSE English. I make mistakes now and then but I can write and people can read it so what's the problem?

Anyway, he told me I'd better use asterixes so I wrote:

'Some **** came to teach us about...'

and he said I could use one of the letters, like this, and he wrote it for me at the top of the page:

Some T***

He gave me a big smile and moved off and this is what I wrote:

'Some T*** came to teach us about creative writing and he told me I couldn't write *W** so I wrote **A* and I thought that'll show the ***T.'

He'd told us to stop when we felt satisfied we had something to share with the others in the group so I didn't write any more.

When I read my bit out (and I had to say "Some tee asterix asterix asterix came..." and so on which meant the others didn't get it) he looked a bit offended and he said he didn't tell me I couldn't write t*** he said I'd better use asterixes cos when you write you've got to think about the reader. Some of the others interrupted him with words like "why", "b******s" and "what the f***'s an asterix?". I thought it was fair comment though cos if I'd thought about me readers I would've written T*** without the asterixes, so I gave him a nod and that got him smiling again.

Once I'd got him smiling again I asked him a question which really got him smiling cos you're encouraged to ask questions. I asked him, if we've got to think about the reader does the reader have to think about us? He said the reader doesn't have to do anything, they don't even have to read us but if they do read us then mostly they can't help thinking about the writer even when sometimes the writer wants the reader to think about the story and not about the writer at all.

This story might have started when I got put in the young offenders' institute.

It might have started when me dad started telling me about all those times Leeds got shafted in the 70s:

Chopper Harris 1970.

Tinkler & Brown 1971.

Being forced to play a crucial Championship game at Molyneux 2 days after winning the FA Cup 1972. (Me dad showed me a newspaper photo of Billy Bremner and Jack Charlton in their hotel beds the morning after the FA Cup before. They look just like I do after a skunk and *Diamond White* night on The Cow and Calf).

Greece 1973.

Revie 1974.

Paris 1975.

Paris 1975. Me dad couldn't get to Greece but he was in Paris that night and he told me he got violent for the first and only time in his life. I never believed that cos he told me about the time he got sent off in a school game for twatting the other school's PE teacher who was reffing. He told me the teacher grabbed him by the ear and tweaked it for shouting FFFFFFFFFFFFF***ING HELL!!!! when his opponent kicked him in the b******s going for a high ball and nowadays it's the teacher who'd get done not him. As if. He told me this story a million times, every time he got merry - Christmas, birthdays, when Leeds won the Championship in 92. He told me about Harris and Tinkler and Greece and Paris and all that a million times too, whenever he got maudlin drunk - Christmas, birthdays, when he got made redundant in 94. And he always ended up telling me about Paris and the one time he made a mistake and had to pay for it when all those bastards are shafting people left right and centre and getting away with it and when you start getting shafted in little ways like Chopper and Tinkler and Molyneux the bastards are just

34

building up to shaft you in big ways like Greece and Paris and it's at that point that all the muscles in his face go slack and he looks like a different person and I tell him I'm tired and I have to go to bed and he never lets me till I've given him a hug.

Some people say Leeds deserved everything they got cos The Mighty Whites had Mighty Black Hearts and the fans were hooligans and me dad'd say this was just the pot calling the kettle black except when he felt depressed, then he'd say the press, the authorities and even the f***ing gods have got it in for Leeds and him personally. I think me dad gave me this over-developed sense of justice and injustice which has got me into trouble over and over again and this is why I say this story might have started when me dad started telling me about all those times Leeds got shafted in the 70s.

But this story might have started when I got put into the young offenders' institute, or the Wheelie Bin as we like to call it cos they wheel us in, feed us garbage, wheel us out again and dump us in the shit. Unless we jump through their hoops first, which is where the creative writing came in.

Paul (the t***) told us to write about something that really got our emotions going. (Creeping up behind me, he says he didn't tell anybody to do anything he just suggests things. Fair comment, but if he thought about his listeners he might understand how whenever some T*** like him suggests something it sounds to us like telling.) As a challenge, he told me to write about something that really got me emotions going without using asterixes so here it is, no asterixes.

Maz and Baz were me best mates. When we played football Maz'd be Speed, Baz'd be Chaps and I'd be Strachs. Fiery little red head. I haven't got a red head but I'm little and fiery. That's how I got me handle BEASTMOUSE. I don't get riled easy and I'm quiet normally but when I think I'm wronged the fires start up and people get burned. It's usually just the verbals though, nowt physical. Except when Maz and Baz decided to turn and support Man U (I bet you're making up your own asterixes here, if you're a Leeds fan).

We were up the Cow and Calf rocks one night (look up next time you're passing and you'll see me name in big letters – BEASTMOUSE). No skunk, just one bottle of *Diamond White* we'd lifted from the offie in town. It were cold so I were having a slash on the rocks when Baz said it. As far as I'm concerned you don't piss on your own cos when the crap comes and the whole world and the gods are against you and your team all you can do is stick together. So I pissed on him. He wasn't keen on that so he went for me. So I splattered him on the rocks. Maz legged it. I looked at Baz and the mess I'd made of him and I felt all these emotions at once. I can't tell you what they are cos when I get like that I don't know who I am and I don't know why I'm feeling the way I'm feeling. It's not mad and it's not brave it's just a big heavy thing inside me that burns and I like the way it feels and hate the way it feels all at the same time.

Paul says this is really good cos I don't need to *tell* the reader what the emotions are it's better to *show* them like the stuff at the end about the heavy weight and the burning. Then Paul tells me to write something that shows us about what I feel when I feel wronged.

It's the Majestyk nightclub in Leeds. It's the trial and the newspapers and the telly, and the world and the gods are ganging up on us again and Istanbul doesn't matter just like Greece and Paris and me dad didn't matter. But we're used to that. This time we're getting shafted in all directions. We're getting shafted by all them who usually like to shaft us but there's one thing, one thing I can't stand, one thing that gets the fires burning and I don't know how to put them out. We're getting shafted by our own. We've no-one to blame this time. This time, the white shirts have got mighty black hearts and all them pots can call us black and we can't call them back.

It's Tuesday morning. I'm hanging around the ground and everybody is turning up for training. I spot them. I want to splatter them on the wall but I probably couldn't. They're hard, or they are if you believe what you read. But they're not going for me and I need that if I'm going to splatter them. Now they're gone, but they've left their cars behind. I've got me spray can with me. I'm going to do some creative writing.

All over their cars, on the doors, the bonnet, the roof, the windows, the boot, I'm spraying:

C***

*U**

**N*

***T

And I don't run away. I want the world to know who the author is.

Paul likes this. He says it's honest and it's powerful and something about eloquence and he says he likes the "delicious irony" of the fact that this is what got me put in the wheelie bin and that I've got a natural talent and that creative writing might be a more positive way of dealing with my emotions than defacing things with graffiti. But that's not the point. Getting banged up for spraying c*** on those c***'s cars isn't ironic it's just sh*te cos it's me the writer that got the attention not what I wrote and I don't want to "deal with my emotions" I want the world to change. Writing can change the world he says. But he would say that wouldn't he? That's his job, giving me a hoop to jump through.

Paul thinks he's made a connection with me. He indulges in a bit of honesty himself, tells me he doesn't like football and he likes Leeds even less. Don't get me wrong, I like the t***. But if he doesn't like football and he doesn't like Leeds, nothing I write will make him understand. End of story.

The trouble with referees is that they just don't care which side wins

Tom Canterbury

The Adventures of Willie Whistle

by Darren Boston

'Penalty!'

In the Theatre of Dreams 60,000 people scream in unison as Gaggs goes flying over the outstretched leg of Pratchett The Hatchet, the infamous tough tackling central defender.

'Goal kick!' shouts the portly but deceptively agile Man In Black.

'You are joking Ref?'

Captain Buckham has run half way across the pitch to confront today's official, Willie Whistle.

'No I'm not David and you're lucky I don't book Gaggsy for diving.' he smiles.

'The Referee's a W**ker', 'Who's the B**tard in the Black?'

The chants rain down on the man in the middle.

Living in a three bedroom terraced house on a less than desirable council estate in a suburb of a certain northern city did not exactly fit the profile of a newly appointed Premier League referee. Local residents were blissfully unaware of their famous neighbour. In this tightly knit community they only knew Willie as the little fat bloke that lived at number 10 who had always been the subject of many of the local kids' pranks and jokes.

'Yo, Mr. Banker. Do you have any good gear for us today?' teenage scuffers would call out as Willie pulled up in his L registered Ford Escort.

'Hey, Willie. You know if you stop supplying us with gear we'll blow the whistle on you!'

They loved teasing the little fat guy at number 10 because he was so straight and honest. He'd probably never even seen a class A drug let alone handled any.

If Willie had a pound for every time he'd had that blow the whistle line since he was a kid he'd be a wealthy man by now, living in a brand new detached house with four bedrooms, en-suite bathrooms, a huge kitchen where wife Betty could create her own delicious recipes, a large garden for son Damian to play footie, double garage to keep his Aston Martin DB7 and Betty's BMW X5, plus a studio and fitness room for 13 year old daughter Julia to perfect her dance routines.

Maybe it was possible to escape his childhood roots and move to a nicer house in a better area, where the fridge and washing machines were kept indoors. Where the street lamps worked and pets roamed the gardens without fear of being strung up or shot at. Wouldn't it be great to start a new career with the game he loved, in a new house, new area, with new neighbours that respected him for who he was and what he did. No more teasing, no more taunting and no more verbal abuse. Then again he had just been appointed referee to England's Premier League. Some things never change!

'Who's your father, who's your father…?'

Even before the second chorus has started Willie is surrounded by the players in red, including a very bald, very angry and very scary looking goalkeeper.

'F***ing hell ref that was a blatant foul.' Scales gesticulates, turning bright pink.

'Come off it ref!' screams Fernando.

Offering his hand to Bryan Gaggs to help him to his feet, Pratchett winks at Willie.

'Good decision ref. Cheers.' he says, and puts his thumb up.

It was a huge decision in a massive title deciding game. Trailing 1 – 0 from a Denis Meinkampf header in the first half, The Reds need a goal and they need one badly. Less than 5 minutes of normal time remains. If The Southerners win they go five points clear at the top of the Premiership. Only two more games left means it looks odds on certain they'll become Champions for the fifth time in a decade.

David Buckham takes his captaincy role very seriously. He ushers his team-mates away to give him time to have a quiet word in the ref's ear.

'Lads, Lads, please let me speak with the ref.' he pleads, waving his arms at them.

Within seconds all of his team have backed off. The opposition players, who have been trying to protect Willie from the marauding red shirts, look round in disbelief. They can't believe the impact Buckham has just had on his team-mates.

'Mr. Whistle. Can I please ask you to reconsider your decision and award us the penalty?' he asks calmly and politely.

'Look Skipper,' says Willie, 'I've already given my decision and there's nothing you can say to change my mind.'

'Ref, I hear that you are a very reasonable man. You must also understand how important this game is to us? So what will it take to change your mind?' Bucks asks.

'What do you mean?' says the bemused official.

'Well put it this way ref. We've not had a penalty against us here in the league for three years and we always like to look after the referees that come here. I know this is your first year in the Premiership and you're trying to do the best job you can. All I'm asking is what incentive would it take for you to change your mind?'

An impatient Hatchet Pratchett approaches the pair in deep conversation. 'What's the problem ref?' he growls.

'Nothing, just leave this one to me thank you.'

Willie waves him away.

Turning to face the Reds' Captain and staring intensely, Willie asks, 'Are you trying to bribe me Mr. Buckham?'

The number 7 looks shocked.

'Of course not Ref. No, all I'm saying is that if you are looking for a nice holiday home in Spain or fancy upgrading your car to a sporty model, then I know people only too willing to help you get them.'

His grin says it all.

Willie's face is getting redder and redder. The sweat starts to pour down his forehead and the back of his neck. He is feeling very uncomfortable and looks completely bewildered. The crowd are getting very impatient.

Processing Jeremy Syke's overdraft request was hardly rocket science, but as part of his job at Tykewell Bank it paid the mortgage and bills for Willie Whistle. Sykes ran a pig farm near Ilkley. His business had been struggling badly ever since the outbreak of mad cow disease, which devastated many farms and dependent industries across the rural north.

'Got a game this weekend Whistle?' John Staples questioned his junior bank clerk.

'Yes, it's the Cup Final for the Yorkshire Amateur League.' Willie always spoke enthusiastically whenever his favourite subject was mentioned, especially games that he was to referee.

'Who's playing?' John asked with no real interest or conviction.

'It's Old Corinthians v Milltown Whites and the Whites are going for the double. So it should be a real cracker.' Willie rubbed his hands in anticipation.

'Yeah right, so when do you start your new career?' was the sarcastic reply.

'We have to report for pre-season training on July 1st and then my first match will be at Ewood Park in the middle of August.'

John continued to mock his work colleague, 'So when are you handing in your notice here and start living the life of Riley?'

'Oh I can't ever see that happening. It's only a short career you know and there's no guarantee on what I'll be earning.' Willie answered, trying to look blasé, secretly thinking how he'd love to tell Staples where to stick his crappy job and leave behind him the constant snide and nasty remarks. Insults he'd put up with over the years from other workers at the bank, but most of all from his boss John Staples - the fact that he was too ugly for TV and far too fat, unless you had widescreen! Too slow to keep up with the pace of the top players and too slow and plodding to make pressure decisions when 40,000 fans were on your back! Willie thought 'I'll show you Staples and the rest of you whose only pleasure in life is to belittle and ridicule others.' The first opportunity that Willie had, after receiving his contract from the Referee's Association, he would walk into the big boss's office at Tykewell Bank's HQ and tell the overweight tycoon exactly what he thought of him and his bank.

The crowd noise has settled to an expectant hum.

Willie continues, 'Let me get this straight. If I award a penalty you will buy me a villa in Spain or a Porsche?'

Willie has always dreamed of owning a place abroad where he and his family could holiday. Somewhere he and Betty could retire to and enjoy the warm Mediterranean sunshine, a far cry from the wet cold winters of England.

'Simple innit?' Buckham replies coolly.

Willie is rattled now. 'Jesus. How long has this scam being going on here? What other referees are in on it?' he thinks. Fifteen years working his way up the ranks of the Referee's Association and reaching now the pinnacle of his career. Willie begins to suspect why The Reds have been so successful in their home fixtures. This is sensational news. This could blow open a can of worms that could ruin the English game. It would also tarnish the reputation of football throughout the world!

'Think about it ref. Why don't you at least consult with your linesman? Jeff's a regular. He knows the score. Why don't you cut him in on the deal?' Buckham adds.

'Christ!' Willie scratches his head, still trying to take it all in.

As a lifelong football lover and a lowly paid clerk in the Tykewell Bank, he is now seriously considering betraying his beliefs, his profession, and his career. All in the space of a manic few minutes.

"Wait here." he signals to Buckham.

The crowd and the opposition players look confused. After nearly three minutes of mayhem followed by calm discussion with the England Captain, Willie Whistle is now walking to his assistant for consultation.

Willie is actually giving himself valuable breathing space. Time to asses the situation and his options. If he gives the penalty and The Reds score then it would be all square in the game but The Southerners could still win the title. If he gives the penalty and Von Mistleroy misses, then it remains "Status Quo" and he now owns a property on the Costa del Sol!

However if he sticks with his original decision then he'll have all the Reds players, their supporters and worst of all Sir Al on his case. He'd also have the football pundits, press and world media with plenty to say about him NOT giving a penalty just when the most famous club in the world need one.

This sort of pressure never occurred at the bank. The biggest decision Willie had to make on any one day is what type of sandwich he'd have for lunch!

'Jeff. I need your help!' he pleads.

'What's on offer?' Jeff Flaggitt replies in a very casual matter of fact manner.

'Uh, a villa in Spain or a sports car.' Willy answers.

'I've got them already Willie. Tell Bucks that I'll settle for £25,000 in my Swiss account as usual.' He smiles.

'But what do I tell the players?' Willie queries.

'Just say I saw it late and book Pratchett for the foul. Don't worry, I'll take the shit. I'm used to it by now.' The assistant referee shrugs his shoulders.

'O – O – OK.' Willie stutters and points to the penalty spot.

Old Trufford erupts. Singing breaks out from the Stepford End 'We're gonna win 2 – 1, we're gonna win 2 – 1.' In almost the same breath, Southern fans chant, 'You don't know what you're doing!'

Now it's the turn of the yellow shirts of London to remonstrate with the man in black and plead for an explanation. Needless to say, Pratchett is shown a yellow card, as is Terry Ennui for virtually man handling Willie.

Once everyone has clamed down, Willie pulls David Buckham to one side and whispers, 'I'm having the Villa but Jeff wants £25,000 in his usual account – OK son?'

'No problem Willie. Welcome aboard.'

'Sorry? What?'

'Welcome aboard I said. I just wanted to be the first to congratulate you on your appointment to the Premier League.'

Derek Upstanding, the Chief Executive of the Referee's Association looks down upon Willie from on high. The pair shake hands as Willie rises stiffly out of the mock leather settee.

'Oh, Thank you Sir.' Willie regains his composure, remembering how it had seemed an eternity sitting outside the committee's meeting room, waiting upon a decision that could quite literately transform his mundane and very ordinary life – forever.

'Thank you very much indeed Sir.' he repeats.

'So now you're going in to the big league what will you spend your money on? A villa in Spain maybe?' the Chief Executive jokes.

'Absolutely not!' snaps Willie.

'Alright Old Boy, I was only joking.'

'I'm sorry Sir. I didn't mean to be rude. The sunshine doesn't agree with me. My skin reacts badly and I come out all blotchy. So I think that idea is a non-starter.' he laughs nervously.

'Never mind Willie, you can always go out and buy a sports car like Beckham's!'

Upstanding breaks into laughter.

Willie isn't entirely sure he understands the joke, if it is a joke.

If this can be termed the century of the common man, then soccer, of all sports, is surely his game... In a world haunted by the hydrogen and napalm bomb, the football field is a place where sanity and hope are left unmolested.

Stanley Rous, 1952

Madski

by Paul Birch

'mad': 1. mentally deranged 2. senseless, foolish 3. angry resentful 4. wildly enthusiastic 5. extremely excited or confused 6. temporarily overpowered by violent reactions emotions etc.

'Leeds': large city in West Yorkshire.

'united': produced by two or more persons or things in combination or from their union or amalgamation.

' Russia': rather large country; used to be communist.

Poliakoff entered his small office and sat down at his even smaller desk. Another dreary day at the Moscow depot of the gas company he unhappily worked for. He slowly turned over the page of the *Yorkshire Evening Post*. These glimpses of a better place arrived in the post on an infrequent basis and he did not want to rush through them. But his eyes quickly scanned over uninteresting minor headlines about a planning controversy in Headingley and falling standards in 'A' level results. They would have been uninteresting if he could have understood them. But as his understanding of English didn't extend to such phrases as "zonal planning criteria" and "planning sub-committees meeting in camera" he passed swiftly on to more recognisable words, such as "score", "nil", "striker" and, of course, "Elland Road".

One day, he promised himself, he would enrol in an English

class. But he had been promising that ever since Perestroika had become old news and now in his early forties he was struggling to be bothered it with it. For the present he would make do with trying to teach himself well enough to read the sports pages and especially the football reports.

For several years now his cousin, Vladim, had been sending him copies of the local newspaper from Leeds, England. Well, the lazy good for nothing durak did when he remembered. He was just the same when he was still living in Moscow. He could never get out of his bed in order to get into work on time. Yet there he was, living in England in what was to Poliakoff undeserved luxury with that woman. Vladim had met her while she was on a week's holiday in Moscow and he was, unusually for him, in work as a waiter at the hotel where she was staying. There was no accounting for taste and it baffled him what the English woman had seen in Vladim.

What made Poliakoff more mad than anything else was that not only had Vladim escaped the dreary existence that had gripped the pair of them since leaving school, the woman bought him tickets each season to watch Leeds United. Lucky bastard! Ever since they had been children they had tried to follow the fortunes of this particular English team. Some boys from Leeds who had been on a school trip to the USSR had traded some Leeds United programmes and a couple of shirts in exchange for a couple of bottles of vodka Vladim had pinched from his granddad. From then on supporting Leeds became their version of teenage rebellion against the state, as if supporting a foreign team and not one of the local Moscow ones would hasten communism into its final death throes. It had been somewhat safer than going on then non-reported anti-government demonstrations and coming back, as some of their friends did, with a sore head thanks to the heavy hand and even heavier club of a policeman, who had not been particularly interested in a discussion on the respective merits of Western style industrial democracy and communist totalitarianism.

As they had entered middle age it had only been economic restraints and not political ones that had prevented them from turning their distant enthusiasm into hands-on reality. Or rather it prevented Poliakoff from seeing his Leeds United in the flesh. While his clerical job at one of the national oil distributors paid for his basic needs it scarcely extended to paying for social activities at the weekend, let alone covering the cost of a trip to Elland Road. Yes, Elland Road, that is where that lucky bastard Vladim will be this weekend, Poliakoff thought. Bastard. It made him even madder to think of that bastard Vladim sitting there every couple of weeks or so watching Leeds. As far as he could make out from the newspaper they were even in the Championship now.

Of course, Vladim had promised that he would send Poliakoff money as soon as possible. But it was difficult, he had said, to get suitable work and he felt that he couldn't ask the woman to give him the money. No, he couldn't ask her, Poliakoff thought angrily, to give him money to send to his not so well-off cousin. But Vladim could ask her to pay for his tickets to watch Leeds. He even had the nerve in one of the rare letters he sent to tell Poliakoff that he should consider himself lucky that there was someone who was able to send him newspapers with match reports in them. As for not being able to find suitable work, well that was a joke. It would be a surprise to see the word "work" in the same sentence as Vladim unless it was accompanied by "out of".

Before he could think of any more reasons to be mad at Vladim he was interrupted by the sound of a pile of letters and parcels dropping onto the desk in front of him.

'Sorry to interrupt your sleep Evgeny Pavlovich.'

It was Grubb the office clerk who was standing in front of him. The sight of the youth's inane grin was not enhanced by the gap between his top front teeth. Several years of free market economy had not yet moved Russian dentistry into the 21st century, or not at least within the meagre budget Grubb would have at his disposal.

'I was not asleep. I was thinking. An activity which I recognise as being alien to you.' Poliakoff sneered back at him.

Grubb, looking down at the desk, saw the English newspaper.

'You were day dreaming about that English football team weren't you?'

'Haven't you got some spots you need to go away and scratch?' Even on good days Grubb got on Poliakoff's nerves. This was not a good day. 'Go on, just sod off.'

'I bet you wished you had more in common with the boss than just his name. I bet you wish you'd had the sense to buy one of the former people's businesses for next to nothing Evgeny.' Grubb taunted.

Pavlovich Poliakoff leaned back in his chair and mused upon his fate. Grubb was right. He did wish that he had the boss's millions as well as his name. That they both had the same three names was down to an accident of parallel ancestry and parental name selection rather than being members of the same family. Poliakoff was almost getting used to the supposedly funny remarks about the two men's respective wealth and position in the world.

'I bet you....'

Grubb's taunting was cut short by a well aimed very old copy of the N to Z volume of the Moscow phone directory striking his temple. Once his eyes had stopped watering, without saying any more he found his way out of Poliakoff's office and disappeared across the damp miserable looking yard towards the other porta-cabins that housed the depot's administrative employees.

If only he had the other Poliakoff's wealth. He wouldn't have any problem going to watch Leeds. Hell, he would do an Abramovich and buy the club and the first thing he would do would be ban that lazy bastard Vladim from the ground. Let him see what it was like to follow your favourite team from newspaper reports in a foreign language. This at least brought a smile to his face. Unfortunately, access to the internet via a PC had not broken through either his financial or his intellectual barriers.

As he began to look through the mail on his desk, the grin on his face began to widen at the thought of that bastard Vladim having to suffer like him in not being able to watch his favourite team. The letters looked to be the usual collection of invoices and complaints.

Most of which he would file, as per company policy, in the waste paper bin in the corner of the room. Nothing got actioned until at least the third request and even then it sometimes needed the influence of the local mafia to move things along on behalf of the creditor or customer – for a fee of course. One package did look different ......

It was addressed to E. P. Poliakoff, but the envelope was of much higher quality than that which he was used to opening. For instance there appeared to be some motif embossed upon it. He was sure he had seen something similar before. Leaving the other letters to one side he began to tear it open. He had made the first tear when he remembered where he had seen the embossed motif before. A few months back the "other, richer" Poliakoff had announced that he would visit the "poorer" Poliakoff's fuel depot by way of a note sent in the same type of envelope. As it turned out the visit had not gone ahead, as happened to many of the visits and trips, both home and abroad, that the "rich" Poliakoff planned and then cancelled at short notice. *Chort!* Poliakoff often wished he was the man's travel agent, as he must be making a fortune on cancelled trips.

'*Chort!*' he uttered to himself again, realising that those morons in the post room in Head Office had got the mail mixed up and sent him the "richer" Poliakoff's mail, and Grubb had been even more of a moron not to have noticed. What should he do? For a brief moment he wondered if he could hide the damage by sticking a piece of sellotape across the tear, but quickly decided that it would fool no-one, not even Grubb. So he decided to continue the tearing, find out was in it, then throw it away and say, if anyone asked, that he had never seen it.

Almost as the plane tickets had landed on the top of the desk, Poliakoff was thinking how he could get some time off work without arousing suspicion. The tickets were obviously meant for the "rich" Poliakoff. No doubt another of his many proposed trips that were cancelled at the last minute. Still he could double-check by phoning Head Office to find out which country the "rich" Poliakoff was due to be in when the tickets were dated.

First Class tickets for a direct flight from Moscow to Manchester, the following week and in the name of Poliakoff. This was just too good an opportunity to miss especially when Leeds United were playing at home. While his geographical knowledge of the UK wasn't brilliant, he did know that Manchester could not be too far from Leeds. In fact compared to distances between places in Russia this was like a stroll down the road to the local vodka shop. Even that lazy bastard Vladim could manage to travel to Manchester to pick him up from the airport.

Given the time differences between Moscow and Leeds he knew he would have to wait until the afternoon to phone his cousin. The time passed slowly, giving him plenty of opportunity to think of all the things that could go wrong with his plan. What if in arriving at the airport he discovered that the ticket had been cancelled, what if someone came looking for the ticket and found him out, what if that lazy bastard Vladim got lost on the way to Manchester airport, what if …….'Oh bollocks,' he thought, ' if it happens it happens.'

At three o'clock in the afternoon he dialled Vladim`s mobile phone number. An impatient few seconds passed before he heard Vladim`s voice.

'Da.'

'Vladim you lazy bastard, it's me Evgeny.'

'Who?'

Lazy and stupid, thought Poliakoff.

'Evgeny!' Poliakoff, shouted at the phone.

'Oh, Evgeny, what do you want?'

'Thank you, yes, I am very well and how are you?' he sarcastically replied. 'Listen,' he continued, 'I've got something to tell you ….What the hell is all that noise in the background? I can hardly hear you.'

'I'm in Starbucks having a coffee.' his cousin shouted back.

Vladim`s raised voiced startled the man who was sitting at the same table in this branch of *Starbucks* in the centre of Leeds. Vladim apologetically shrugged his shoulders at the man.

'Moscow. A long way to hear.' he said in a strong accent.

The man at the table was called Harry Alexander and was a freelance journalist who tried, not very successfully it had to be said, to specialise in football stories. In fact, he was in Leeds that morning in the expectation of seeing one of the Elland Road office employees who sometimes gave him some gossip he had picked from one of the players. But the chap hadn't turned up and Harry was about to leave when Vladim`s half apology for nearly bursting his eardrum made him stay out of idle curiosity.

He knew, or thought he did, what was being said as the man next to him, who he now assumed to be Russian, was repeating out loud, very loud, almost everything his caller was saying.

'No, speak in English Evgeny. It will be good practice for you.'

Back in Moscow Poliakoff was already beginning to wonder whether all the bother was worth it. But he needed Vladim, so he decided to humour him and hesitantly began.... 'I have first class ticket to Manchester and I need you to collect me on Friday.'

'You are coming to Manchester First Class on Friday.' Vladim repeated.

'Secret, no one to know.' The last thing Poliakoff wanted was for Vladim to blab to someone about the windfall plane tickets. 'Ticket for me I want you to buy Leeds United, game Saturday.'

'What did you say Poliakoff? Secret. You want to buy Leeds United?'

At this statement Harry's idle curiosity suddenly began to buck its ideas up. He was sure he had read or heard that name recently. As he eavesdropped what bits of the conversation he could, he tried to remember where.

'No you idiot,' Poliakoff angrily shouted in Russian, losing patience with his cousin, 'buy ticket for Leeds United game. I want to see it Saturday. Doesn't matter which seat. I will pay any price. I will explain everything when I see you. But remember, top secret.' Durak! Poliakoff said under his breath.

'Ok, ok. I get it. Collect you Friday at Manchester Airport. Go to Leeds United. You will pay any price but no one to know. Details later. No problem. Listen, I can't talk here. Call me back in a couple of hours.'

'Yes. I'll call you back. Do svidanya.' said Poliakoff, thinking that no way would that lazy bastard pay for the cost of a call.

Vladim finished his drink and left the coffee shop, leaving Harry Alexander racking his brains trying to remember where he had heard the name Poliakoff. This seemed too good to be true. Had he really heard that some Russian was planning to come incognito to look over Leeds with a view to buying it? Price no object? He then remembered he had to pay his gas bill while he was in Leeds. At this he also remembered where he had heard the name Poliakoff before. In an article about potential foreign buyers of English Premier League clubs his name had appeared in a list of Russians who had similar amounts of money as Roman Abramovich. But it had said that this guy was more interested in Italian clubs, which hadn't made sense at the time, given that most of them were in a worse financial state than English clubs. But that could have been a smoke screen .....

Over the following few hours Harry tried to find out more about this shadowy Russian magnate so that he could verify the conversation he had just overheard. His somewhat limited contacts in the world of football finance i.e. none, were of little use. All he managed to confirm from a few web sites was that this Russian did exist, but there did not appear to have been any recent reports of him being remotely interested in any English clubs. In the hope of finding out more he decided to run the risk of losing an exclusive story by contacting someone he knew at one of the nationals.

Harry made several phone calls, unwittingly prompting rumours about a mysterious buyer for Leeds United (which it had to be said .was almost a weekly occurrence). However, rumour fatigue had already started to have an impact and so on a national basis any flicker of interest was soon extinguished by more credible reports, for example of plans by Chelsea's Russian to buy the Juventus forward line when the next transfer window opened.

But the story did manage to use its last breath to crawl into the Board Room at Elland Road, where any potential takeover reports were given at least one hearing, however fictional they first appeared. Looking for a way to offload at least some of the current debt used to buy the club or even better make a profit from this football version of pass-the-parcel, the current incumbents – several versions on from the original takeover in the relegation year – were willing to explore any opportunity. Investigations were initiated and within a few hours Harry was sat in a quiet pub on the outskirts of Leeds relating back to the Leeds Chairman what he had heard earlier in Starbucks.

So as not to restart the rumours, agreement was reached that Harry and not a club official would watch out for the Russian's arrival at Manchester Airport and report back to the Chairman, in exchange for the exclusive story should any takeover go ahead.

But almost as soon as he was back in his car the Chairman was on his mobile phone organising a limousine and a five star hotel. 'Incognito my backside', he thought. Nor was he going to rely on a journalist, and a not very good one at that, to keep tabs on this potential cash windfall. He hadn't got where he was without getting his retaliation in first. 'We'll give this Russian the treatment – top transport, top accommodation, top food –Chicken Kiev, or whatever it is they eat,' he told his fellow Board members, 'and woe betide anyone who puts a foot wrong and jeopardises the deal.'

As Vladim was buying one return and one single rail ticket to and from Manchester Airport and wondering where in the house his cousin would sleep that evening Poliakoff eased himself into his first class seat and began to feel a little more relaxed. He had felt sure that someone would have challenged him when he had arrived at Moscow airport to check in for the flight. Thank goodness it was a British Airways flight and staff – they wouldn't know one Poliakoff from another. An hour or so later, with a few glasses of champagne inside him, he was feeling even more relaxed. The alcohol began to overcome his worry and he even started to believe that he would get away with the excuse he had given for not being able to go into work over the following few days (forgetting that this was the third time his great Aunt Anastasia in Minsk had died and he had had to attend the funeral). He began to enjoy the flight and think of the following day when at last he would get to watch his team in the flesh for the first time. As he slowly slipped into an alcohol induced sleep somewhere over northern Germany Evgeny Pavlovich was blissfully ignorant of the feverish activity the phone call to his cousin had set in motion.

At Elland Road the new Board was almost beside itself with excitement as the prospect of a profitable transaction with a Russian, who may have more money than sense. Only recently had they taken charge of the club, having not really expected the previous Board to accept their offer. An opportunity of making a quick profit was just too good to miss.

As Poliakoff's plane was coming into land the following afternoon he was unaware of two of the three parties who were waiting for him. His flight had been thankfully uneventful and still no one had questioned his right to be on the plane. As he finished his sixth glass of champagne he thought to himself that he could get used to this first class style of travel.

After landing, his passage through customs and immigration was equally uneventful. 'Hell,' he thought, 'I am going to get away with this. Now, as long as that lazy bastard Vladim is there waiting for me things should be ok.' His brief moment of concern was unnecessary. He could now see Vladim waving to him from behind a barrier next to a group of smartly dressed men, one of whom was holding a sign that spelt his name out in Russian. Poliakoff looked at Vladim and pointed questioningly at the sign with his name on it. Harry, too, had seen these men and the sign. Although Harry couldn't read Russian, the fact that he recognised one of the men as the Leeds Chairman confirmed to him that he had been double crossed. Before he could decide what to do he saw the Chairman, who had seen Poliakoff point at his sign, stride forward towards two men who were hugging each other. Harry recognised one of them as the man in the coffee shop. He moved slightly forward to get a better look at the other man and at the same time reached inside his jacket pocket for something.

Vladim too recognised the Chairman from photographs he had seen in the local paper over recent weeks, while the latest change of ownership was being enacted. The Chairman blurted out some rushed words of welcome and spoke of looking forward to a mutually beneficial visit A young woman who was next to him began to translate what the Chairman was saying. But because the Chairman was speaking too quickly she was about four sentences behind all the time. Poliakoff's little understanding of English was running out at roughly the same rate as his anxiety at being found out as a fraud was increasing and the woman talking at him at the same time made him even more confused. As his arm was vigorously pumped by the Chairman's handshake he looked around for the imminent arrival of the police. But instead of being handcuffed he was gripped by a round of handshakes as he was apparently introduced to the other men who were with the first man who had shaken his hand.

Vladim, who had been almost pushed to one side, may have been lazy but he was quick on the uptake. He heard Poliakoff begin to protest at what was happening and give himself up.

'Keep quiet you fool,' he snapped, out of earshot of the woman who had now given up trying to translate the Chairman's rapid fire words, 'let me do the talking. I think they believe that you are the rich Poliakoff and that you are here to buy Leeds United. Let's keep this going as long as we can. We don't want any trouble here. We can sort out the mistake later. It sounds like there's a limo waiting for us and we're being put up in a luxury hotel tonight and also something about Chicken Kiev.'

Vladim stepped in to interrupt the greetings that were becoming increasingly more ingratiating and quickly explained in as good English as he could that Mr Poliakoff was suffering from a bad throat infection and was under doctor's orders to talk as little as possible for the next few days and that as his personal assistant he would be speaking for him.

Harry was standing back, taking in what was happening. As he watched and listened more he smiled and on overhearing Malmaison Hotel being mentioned he decided to set off back to Leeds. On the way back he phoned the hotel and booked a room.

Vladim needed some time alone with Poliakoff to agree what they were going to do next. So in the limo Vladim explained to the welcoming party that Mr Poliakoff would like to rest that evening after his journey and contact his business colleagues back in Moscow. The Chairman seemed a little put out at not being able to start discussions there and then but not wishing to seem over keen agreed that the following morning a car would pick them up prior to a tour of the club's "excellent" training facilities and Elland Road itself before the game.

When they eventually got in the hotel room and locked the door Poliakoff dropped into a chair and buried his head in his hands.

'Chort! What the hell is going on? I'm going to be arrested, I know it. I should never have taken those tickets. I must have been mad.'

Vladim snapped back at him.

'Listen. They think you are the rich Poliakoff, here to buy Leeds United. If you don't panic we can carry this off. They think you can't speak at the moment so you can leave all the talking to me. I'll tell them that you don't want any fuss. You just want to have a look round the ground at this stage, see the game tomorrow and then return to Moscow on the flight tomorrow evening. No problem.'

Vladim was almost starting to believe himself.

'No problem? No problem? Not only am I going to get arrested, when they eventually release me from here, there'll be a welcoming party in Moscow and their car won't be taking me to the Rossiya Hotel!'

'Look. As I see it we've got a choice. You can give yourself up now and spend the next few days staring at a concrete cell wall, eating prison food and wondering why your cell mate keeps smiling at you (Poliakoff noticed that the "we" had suddenly become a "you" when his cousin spoke about giving oneself up) or we can try and bluff it out. Stay the night in this posh hotel, get tour of Elland Road, have the best seats in the house for the game and get chauffeured back to the airport. We'd be mad not to try.'

Vladim was already seeing himself comfortably seated in the Directors` box.

More whining and whimpering noises continued to emanate from the now curled up form on the large king-sized bed.

'Evgeny Pavlovich! If you don't pull yourself together right now I'm going give you a slap and then turn you in myself.'

It was a race as to whose colour drained the quicker from their cheeks as Vladim`s anger at Poliakoff was interrupted by a loud knock on the door.

'Chort!' they both said in unison.

The seconds of indecision between them seemed as long as a lifetime's banishment in the old Soviet gulag.

The knock was repeated even louder, but this time it was accompanied by a voice neither of them recognised.

'Come on, open the door. I know you are in there.'

'Oh chort …..You'd better answer it Vlady. …………...'

The Directors` lounge was crowded at half time as Harry sidled up to the Chairman's side.

'He looks to be enjoying himself.' he said, nodding towards Poliakoff, who was tucking into his eighth prawn sandwich. 'I understand the Board took him and his special adviser up to the club's state of the art training ground this morning followed by the VIP tour of the ground. Introduced him to some of the players I expect. Wouldn't be surprised if some of them were already worried about their place in the team, what with him and all his millions to spend on new talent. Wonder if that thought has spurred them on to a two-nil lead this half? Have you done a deal with him yet?'

Surprised, the Chairman turned and looked straight into Harry's face.

Realising that the Chairman was wondering how he had got into the lounge Harry said, 'Surprised to see me? I've still got my press pass if you are wondering how I got in.' Harry's manner was very matter of fact. 'Thought we'd agreed that the ground would be left clear for me.'

'Harry, mate. You know how it is. Couldn't take the chance of blowing it. A lot of money at stake old son. Too much at risk to leave things with you.' the Chairman condescendingly replied.

'Fair enough, I understand.'

'Good of you to see it that way Harry.'

'Been speaking to some of the chaps from the nationals. Seems you have been telling them about some big announcement that is going to be made about a change in the future ownership of the club. Appears that comrade Poliakoff's "special adviser" has been making very encouraging noises about his boss being very impressed with the set up and likely wanting to come to an amicable financial arrangement as soon as possible about the club.' Harry said with a broad smile that he was finding increasingly more difficult to stop.

'You know I couldn't comment on that Harry.' The Chairman answered smugly.

'Yes I expect they have their columns almost finished as we speak. I expect your stock with them has gone up quite a bit. Shame if you had to explain that you had got it all wrong and that there was no buyer after all.'

'What do you mean?'

'Spoken to our friend comrade Poliakoff, have you?' Harry asked.

'Hardly call him a "comrade" with all his roubles. Besides, he doesn't speak English, that's why we've been discussing things with his special "adviser".'

'Oh, I think you'll find that comrade Poliakoff speaks excellent English. Well, it says that on his website that I was looking at on Thursday.'

Harry couldn't help grinning even more as he said this.

'No, really I've tried. He doesn't speak English.' The Chairman replied irritably.

'Oh you mean that Poliakoff, over there? Yes, I agree. That one doesn't speak English.'

'What do you mean "that" Poliakoff? How many are there?'

The Chairman was now wondering what Harry was on about.

'Well, there's the poor one here and the rich one back in Moscow.'

Harry was finding it hard to contain himself.

The Chairman was becoming confused.

'What?'

'That individual, my dear chap, is, I grant you, called Evgeny Pavlovich Poliakoff. Unfortunately for you and your cronies over there trying to ingratiate themselves with him, he is not the Poliakoff version that they thought they have been entertaining so royally since he got here. No, I think you'll find he is a minor clerk in the rich Poliakoff's empire, who just happens to have exactly the same name as his boss.'

Harry took from his pocket a photo of the rich Poliakoff he had printed off from his website. It was the same photo that Harry had taken from his jacket pocket to look at the previous day at the airport and which had made him realise that the man, whose hand the Chairman had been so vigorously shaking, was not the right man. Harry handed the photo to the Chairman.

'You just couldn't be bothered to check anything yourself. What's more, last night in his hotel room, kindly paid for by the club, I signed up from his "special adviser", who happens to be his unemployed illegal immigrant cousin, the rights to the story of how the Chairman and Board of Leeds United and a number of major national newspapers were taken in by a Russian invoice ticker. See you later. You can keep the photo.'

As Harry walked away the Chairman's face was as white as a Leeds shirt thirty seconds before kick off……..A brief conversation later and so were the rest of the Board's.

Evgeny Pavlovich's flight back to Moscow later that evening was as uneventful as the first. Vladim had been right. They had been able to bluff it out. In fact it seemed that the Chairman and his colleagues were in as big a rush to get him back to the airport as he was. Shame that the limo must have been being used elsewhere. Still, the taxi was better than those in Moscow. He waved goodbye to Vladim and Harry as he went through into the departure lounge.

A little while later, as he sank back into his comfy first class seat, holding his first glass of champagne of the flight, he was accompanied into his dreams by memories of the four goals scored by Leeds that afternoon with no reply and how he cheered and screamed in celebration of every one of them. The people around him must have thought he was mad. He was …. mad for Leeds.

Supporters' rites

by Helen Morrison

(Sunday, England are playing someone)

There's still a cross on display to commemorate a martyr's death
though doubtless few think of that now. There's still singing
to focus minds on the cause and a liturgy (of sorts) with
surprisingly little doubt about the words. There's
a dress code bearing rather more logos than
Sunday best. Libations are poured
more freely and expressions
of agony and ecstasy,
overt, monosyllabic
Speaking in
tongues
rarely
departs
from
Anglo – Saxon
A little incense would
be welcome.
It would
relieve
the
smell
of sweat
Flower
arrangements
however would
be lost among the
bunting and the face paint
Afterwards hugs of fraternal love
are not unknown though the signs exchanged
are not those of peace only. Passing motorists taunt the
disappointed and dejected as they sprawl outside the glum pubs

For Harry & St. George

by Simon Chandler and David Gill

Dramatis Personae Non-grata:

THE ORGANISER OF FUN - A *Drambuie*-stained idiot

THE BOSS - A weeble-shaped leader of men

THE CHEF - An outbreak of botulism waiting to happen

THE TRAINEE CHEF - A callow youth tentatively learning The Ways Of The Packet And Tin

THE ASSISTANT MANGLER - Working at The George Hotel in order to meet new people and to avoid an awkward investigation into Crimes Against Humanity and Small Animals

COLM THE IRISH – who doesn't appear (by special arrangement)

GUESTS – Lost Souls (various), doomed to stagger this Earth

PARROT – a brightly coloured talking bird

RAT/WOODLOUSE (non-speaking)

The kitchen of the George Hotel. Dinnertime. Tomorrow, England depart for the World Cup Finals in Germany. Other than that, it is an ordinary day – filth coats every surface; a rat is writhing in agony having mistaken a scone for food. THE TRAINEE CHEF is halfway through a precariously piled stack of chipped and cracked oven-proof baking dishes, scraping their congealed and blackened contents into a large plastic dustbin. THE CHEF contemplates the scene whilst absently wringing the neck of an anorexic, already dead and featherless chicken.

THE ASSISTANT MANGLER marches in, shiny black stilettos clacking urgently against the grimy terracotta tiling.

ASS MANGLER: What are we going to do about dinner now that the Non-alcoholic Ale Pie's done a Hiroshima?

CHEF: [calling to Trainee] We still got those cocking out-of-date Pot Noodles?

TRAINEE: Yer, they're out the back with the microchips and Gourmet Pet Food.

CHEF: We'll cocking give em that then.

CHEF plunges the chicken, wrung neck, lolling head, wattle and all into a vat of congealing soup.

ASS MANGLER: It's supposed to be something 'Traditional

English.'

CHEF: Well give it a cocking Traditional English name then.

TRAINEE: How about "Horse's Arse Stew an Chips – a real dog's dinner"?

ASS MANGLER: Hmmm... "Huntsman's Casserole with curly noodles and deep-fried Julienne potatoes." [writing it down] Traditional English, with a contemporary twist. It'll do nicely.

 She turns smartly on her heel and marches out.
The moment she leaves, a portly balding goblin pops its head timidly round the filthy-fingered door frame. A small wee voice pipes up from somewhere above a cascade of wobbling chins.

BOSS: Hello team! Is my dinner ready yet? I could jolly well eat a proverbial horse.

CHEF: I've told you to keep yer cocking nose out of my kitchen when I'm creating.

BOSS: Ahaha, I can see things are a little busy here. I'll pop back later. Must put up the World Cup fixtures chart on the foyer notice board.

He leaves, wobbling.

CHEF: [to trainee] Get on with the Huntsman's Casserole then – an don't bother with those cocking tomato ketchup sachets. I don't get paid to do fiddly stuff. Who do they think I am – cocking Gordon Ramsey!?

THE TRAINEE inches past the hot angry maw of the pie oven, eyeing it nervously. A chance lick of flame illuminates the tomb-like interior. THE TRAINEE doesn't see the solitary Tee-totaller's Ale Pie smouldering in the black depths.

As the culinary conjuror and his apprentice go about their craft, the scene wobbles and shifts to a mildewed dusty turret clinging to the rear of the castle. THE ORGANISER OF FUN is just rising to begin his day's toil.

ORGANISER: Errrrrghhhhh.

The voice gurgles uncertainly from tonsils gummed with *Guinness* and fragments of Scampi Fries. Lungs ravaged by accompanying Liam Gallagher, that paragon of English gentlemanly-ness and chivalry, in an unwise falsetto version of "Champagne Super Nova", struggle to release another Neanderthal articulation.

ORGANISER: Urrrghhh, my eyes don't work. Where are my legs? Where did that tattoo come from?

The phone rings. A palsied, ashtray-stained hand reaches out and dislodges an out-of-date Pot Noodle container from its precarious perch atop a discarded David Gray CD. It falls on a woodlouse, crushing it with a thud and an inaudible shriek. THE ORGANISER answers with a laid-back eloquence.

ORGANISER: Whaaaargh?

BOSS: Good afternoon. Lovely to talk with you again. We were wondering if you wouldn't mind popping down and doing something with the guests for a little while – if that's not inconvenient.

ORGANISER: S'pose. Give me half an hour. I need to brush my teeth and shave my tongue.

BOSS: Splendid! Whenever you're ready. Be happy!

THE ORGANISER tosses the cordless receiver into a bin liner protruding pregnantly from the waste bin.

ORGANISER: [resignedly] Oh well, better get my arse together and go down to my public, for I AM THE ORGANISER!

Thunder rolls and lightning crackles.

The dining room. Two hours later.
GUESTS are desperately thrusting forks in search of the

remaining chunks of reconstituted beef lurking in the depths of the primordial Pet Food and Pot Noodle sludge. THE ASSISTANT MANGLER emerges through the double doors to gasps of terror. She wears tight leather shorts over mountainous ridges of bottom, a bullet-proof brassiere and matching blood-stained jackboots. She spits tobacco juice at a passing kitten, adjusts her jewel-encrusted eye patch and croaks forth.

ASS MANGLER: Right scum, get out. It's FUN TIME in the ballroom and we've got to hose these tables down.

THE MANGLER aims a flip of her Cat-o'-Nine-Tails at an abandoned Great Aunt. A dislodged artificial limb spins into the air and cracks against a grimy window-pane.

ASS MANGLER: [to the terrified Guest] You'll pay for that. See me after Hymn Singing for Punishment.

TERRIFIED GUEST: No, please mercy etc.

ASS MANGLER: None of that. You chose the accommodation, you must accept the consequences. A spell sandpapering the bed linen might teach ye the error of yer ways!

PARROT: [perching on shot putter-sized shoulder] Pieces of Eight! Pieces of Eight!

The Kitchen. TRAINEE is holding a newspaper in one hand,

reading an article listing the various bone-breaks, psychoses, neuroses, and domestic/public scandals of the England squad players. With the other hand he is scraping at a huge cooking pot with a rasp, removing tiny bits of noodle, horsemeat, and perhaps even fragments of huntsman. CHEF is serving slabs of chicken and vegetable soup onto plates with a spatula. A timid baldy head on the end of a non-existent neck peeps round the doorframe.

BOSS: Splendid dinner chef. The guests are speechless. Is my dinner ready yet? Oh! Err, is that thingy-bob at the back supposed to have smoke coming out of it?

Smoke belches from the oven.

CHEF: Course not, it's cocking on fire innit?

TRAINEE: [panicking] Aren't you going to put it out!?

CHEF: Wot with? My cock? Yer cocking arsefeck. It's a cocking inferno is that.

BOSS: Ahahaha, jolly good – keep up the good work!

He leaves, wobbling quickly.

CHEF: [to trainee] Where do we keep the cocking fire blanket?
TRAINEE is nowhere to be seen.

The Turret. Same time. THE ORGANISER has one sock on. Tartan, with holes. Its partner, pale yellow with a faded picture of Homer Simpson saying 'Doh!', is half way on but refusing to negotiate the instep and ankle. A hot breeze accompanied by a flock of curly black moths' wings billows in through the window.

The Ballroom, moments later. The guests have been wheeled in and are propped up around the room. ASS MANAGER has an amusingly-shaped balloon in her hand.

ASS ORGANISER: Right. Good. Ten of you, over there on the far wall. Ten of you here with me. Now!

THE GUESTS stand, or lie, motionless. ASS MANGLER cracks the whip. THE GUESTS yelp and as one dash to the far side of the room.

The Turret. Same time. THE ORGANISER abandons the yellow sock. He rummages under the bed, finds one shoe.

The Ballroom. Moments later. TEN GUESTS are lined up with THE MANGLER. Each has hot red weals around eye, cheek, chin.
ASS MANGLER: Are we ready now? Let's play *World Cup Final* -

England vee Germany. I'm reffing and GERMANY VILL VIN!!

The whip cracks and the balloon pirouettes into the air. It halts abruptly, then begins to float gently downwards. One foolish GUEST representing the England side, a young Goth, clad entirely in black but for a single red contact lens, thinks she can gather the balloon and make for the French windows, beyond which, in her wild imagination, lies the fabled Germany goal-line. The cat lashes out and the Goth now has matching scarlet eyes.

PARROT: [flapping] Polly want a cracker! Polly want a cracker!

The balloon drifts into free space.

MANGLER: [to the German 'side'] *Vorwärts! Vortschreiten! Schnell!*

The "German" guests, moaning deeply, advance upon the balloon which is bobbing to rest by the feet of the English team. The English are now huddling together on the safety in numbers principal. One anarchistic soul, a ginger-haired man in a green tweed suit, raises a purple Doc Martin and kicks at the balloon. The cat barks and the man is no more, simply a smoking ginger wig where the Docs once stood.

The Turret. Simultaneous. Batting wildly at the moth wings

which are now engulfing the room, THE ORGANISER drops his one shoe and gropes for the door. He pulls desperately but it won't budge. Something is jamming it. In the sooty blackness he cannot see Homer Simpson peeping out from under the door and saying 'Doh!.'

The Ballroom. Hot, intense moments have passed. The English are scattered and the Germans have the balloon. THE MANGLER bestrides all; eyepatch glinting, brassiere heaving, lederhosen rippling. The Cat-o'-Nine Tails whirls about the ballroom, sparks flying as its nine vicious barbs strike walls, chandelier, harpsichord. The ancient keyboard plays a ringing mangled chord. In response THE MANGLER lets forth an excruciating High C, an eldritch primal scream.

At once the French windows burst open and eleven Valkyrie maidens riding great bat-winged Kraken swoop in. The German players are swept up as the English are cut down in their ranks. The balloon is borne towards the goal – the great stone fireplace, above which hangs the Turner portrait of Sir Harry Van de Simple Poppleton, Founder of The George Hotel.

The Turret. Simultaneous. THE ORGANISER battles his way back to the open window. Outside, the sky has turned purple and blue, heaving like a great pullulating bruise. Below him, gigantic white-hot arms of flame shoot out from the kitchen across the hotel grounds. Then, though his ears quail and collapse at the very sound, he hears the horribly transformed yet horrifyingly recognisable voice of THE MANGLER, Die Erste Dame of Doom, leading the Hellish Wagnerian Orchestra of Valhalla in an Operatic Gangsta Rap.

Then, just as he is about to choose a quick death in the kitchen flames, he spies a soft golden light on the horizon, just above the skirt of green which marks the deep forest boundary. A gentle sonorous sound reaches him beyond the din. A distant trumpet call. Then hoofbeats. Getting nearer...nearer...

The Ballroom. Simultaneous. The bowed and bloody English have been backed into the fireplace. Behind them, the hearth opens to reveal the fiery mouth of hell. A "German" GUEST, Mrs Twentywell from Withernsea, has the balloon. She raises a peep-toed sandal, ready to strike. THE MANGLER raises the cat.

Then the English rise as one. They see through the shattered French window a glorious apparition galloping across the grounds. THE BOSS, in gleaming gold armour and helm, astride a great white stallion, a long white lance held before him, the shield of St.George held across his breast.

BOSS: [crying passionately] FOR HARRY AND ST. GEORGE!!!!

The lance cuts a vicious swathe through the air as the magnificent war-horse crashes across the field, nostrils flaring brilliant red against the pulsating white. The Germans, THE MANGLER, Valkyrie, Kraken and all quail at the sight. Then lance, shield, helm and BOSS clatter to the ground as the horse halts with an abruptness that shakes the heart.

A shoe has been thrown. A metatarsal broken.

The Turret. Seconds later. Seeing all, THE ORGANISER forces the window shut and retires into his blackened room.

ORGANISER: Bugger this for a game of soldiers.

He goes back to bed, opens a bottle. He peers down the neck. Huge waves violently toss the foamy surface of the midnight black ocean inside. He closes his eyes, takes a huge gulp of air, and dives in.

The turret roof collapses. Masonry falls onto woodlouse.

The Ballroom. Simultaneous. THE MANGLER shrieks in triumph. The whip cracks and the peep-toed sandal strikes. Balloon and English hit the back of the hearth. The great maw swallows them whole, cackles, and burps.

Outside, the grounds. Simultaneous. THE BOSS picks his face out of a muddy puddle. He despairs as he watches the turret collapse and the red and white ensign of St. George shrivels and perishes in the flames. Then it comes. The shriek of triumph. That guttural

Nordic voice, gasping and hoarse with ecstasy. First creeping across the grounds, enveloping THE BOSS as he tries to shield his ears, then speeding up and over the deep dark forest, over the hills and beyond, to trumpet across the length and breadth of Albion and ultimately over the entire world, the gloating and sneering roll-call of England's fallen heroes:

THE MANGLER: *Princess Di, Maggie Thatcher, Tony Blair, Brian Clough, Geoffrey Boycott, Delia Smith, Bernard Manning – ARE YOU LISTENING?! Pam Ayres, Sherlock Holmes, Eddie The Eagle, Morecambe and Wise, Florence and Zebedee, La-la and Po! YOUR BOYS TOOK A HELL OF A BEATING! YOUR BOYS TOOK A HELL OF A BEATING!!!!*

Schmucked

by Simon Chandler & David Gill

Thrust by Helen Morrison

Sensible specs
grey hair
a whole grey body,
they said of one.

The other, puzzlingly slow to rise
when his lads do well
as if older than his 56 years.

Unlikely candidates these
for the leadership of England,
yet the author of bonkbusters
and a trio of foreign beauties
can confirm
that these two
do not lack thrust.

France 2 England 1

How did I feel? Well, bitter rawness and spittle-projecting rage briefly made their customary appearance, but these were only hiding a more unpleasant feeling – that of being made a sucker, a patsy, a one-born-every-minute feckwit.

I had slipped quietly into this tournament deliberately under-exposed. I'd avoided newspaper talk of possible frail groins and creaking abductors. If *5 Live* turned to Mark Lawrenson for expert analysis of Christmas trees, 4-4-2s or Erickson's Subtle Tactical Nous, I turned off. When the tournament opened, my studied indifference to the opening ceremony hysteria would have made Alan Shearer seem exuberant. My first contact with the game was the game.

I explained this attitude to my colleagues, and even to myself, as being due to work commitments (as if my "work" and my "commitment" can exist in the same sentence without eyebrows raising or even guffaws exploding) and to a busy social life, excuses which my regular mysterious disappearances persuaded them to accept without the raising of brow or explosion of guffaw. The real reason was a determination not, ever, ever to fall for it again. Never. No more self-delusion. My whim, despite evidence, is to consider myself an intelligent enough person, not compelled to follow the herd, capable of thinking for myself. Yet, and this is hard to write, I believed Graham Taylor could win The World Cup. I thought that Kevin Keegan was a motivational genius on a par with Nelson Mandela or Bob Geldof. I nurtured the impression that El Tel would pull every Cockney-sparrer-wide-boy trick in the manual, legit or otherwise, to, first, bring the English bacon home in 96, then second, to cook the Gallic goose in 98. You can see clearly now, I'm sure, what was always true, that these men were the kind of slipshod, second-rate, Spanish street market 'Roonee' fake replica jokers that must have had Cloughie *You are a bluddy disgrace*-ing in confused horror. So, no more. This time I would watch the game calmly, serenely, detached. We seemed good enough to do ok. Make them feel they've been in a game. Give a decent account of ourselves. A modest, realistic ambition, acceptable to a reasoned mind. We weren't going to win, and I welcomed the realisation. I wouldn't have to get all sweaty and annoyed about this one, just watch the game and enjoy the contest, win or lose.

Bastardos! I fell for it again.

It was the spin you see. For Sven, read Tony. Like The Smiler, The Swede was surely going to be different. No throwback to outdated ideas and tired old methods of operation. This guy would be modern, European and efficient. No hurled teacups, no swearing, just softly spoken words and cappuccino. In press conferences he would smile in a way that suggested he knew more than he was letting on, that he had profound thoughts and hidden depths we could only guess at but that when the time came we would see, and applaud the inevitable glory resulting. Oh the quiet confidence made us thrill at the prospects for our exciting young team. All this and glamour too! He made the previous lot look grey and awkward, in their ill-fitting suits and with their drab wives. This man was the future, with his sleek suits, post post-modern transparent spectacles and power-dressing soccer-savvy wife with the smouldering eyes and body to lie to your bank manager for. It could only get better and better from here on in.

Now, with the benefit of hindsight I admit, I see them for what they really are; Tricksters, Charlatans, Snake Oil Salesmen, Emperors with their kit off, The Devil's Favourite Shysters. Which makes me a dreadful shmuck, because I bought it all. Again.

The game itself followed the familiar formula. Players walk onto pitch each holding child's hand (representing The Future, or a warning against going off with strange men, I'm not sure which);

87

close-ups of players looking determined, probably due to fierce desire to win, but possibly due to strain of remembering words to anthem, or singing it in an impossibly high key. Whistle blows, crowd roars and England launch into a series of misplaced passes, leading to groans and abuse of culpable player (usually a Neville), who you wouldn't have picked for a game in the park never mind an international. Then, the unexpected goal. It is at this moment that the carefully constructed insouciance that I took with me into the bar collapses, like a footballer outside a lap dancing bar at 3 a.m. We were winning, France were losing. WE were WINNING, FRANCE were LOSING. 1-0! To us! Suddenly I was surrounded by friends and strangers alike casting their Englishness aside and hugging and kissing like the French. It was all mad and excitable and I allowed myself to become carried away on a wild surge of hope.

The surge surged further as the minutes went by. France should be panning us. But they're not. They're playing like us. Perhaps they've all spent too many years playing in *The Premiership*. They're crap. They don't look like scoring in a month of Junes. We're crap too, but there's no pressure. We can do this. If the players have a tenth of the adrenalin pumping through them as we the fans have, we can take them. Go for it. We've got them.

Football's a really easy game to play sitting on top of a bar stool, I know. I mean, the French are touch players, instinctive. If you hang off them and give them time and space to build up their confidence, they'll eventually get yer. But that's just armchair manager talk. What do we know? The English hang off. Slowly,

slowly, the French begin to make inroads. I mean, if we don't pose any attacking threat at all, if we don't have an outlet to relieve the pressure, force them back, make them cautious, the dam will break. Surely? But what do we know? Ok, defend deep if you must but don't give away a free kick on the edge of the box in the last minute. Oh, all right then, put a man on the post. No? Well what the hell do we know?

It is at this point that we see Sven, The Man With The Plan, come to the fore. A suggestion of a frown crosses that wide expanse of forehead. Clearly, Great Thoughts are being thought. Any moment The General will speak and the French will be thrown back, the unfortunate goal forgotten in a flurry of English passing and shooting. We have strikers, the only way now is forward. The command rings out, quietly and politely from the immaculate manager – 'Fall back! Retreat! Defend for your lives, it's what we do best. (The Nevilles! The Nevilles! The crowd point and shriek in horror!). A draw will do! Up! Up! For Harry and Saint Draw!!' Oops. The writing on that wall could be seen from space. We can't defend. Our players are like wind-up toys, you point them in any direction and off they go like the clappers. They can't run backwards, they're just not designed for it. So, although we hoped and prayed for otherwise, we know the game is up, even before that last agonisingly obvious pantomime of a back pass finishes the job.

The whole pub as one falls heavily into their chairs and beer. I can see a girl in a really skimpy England top fighting to hold back her tears of frustration. A bearded someone says, 'Oh well, it's only the first game.' A quietly spoken gent utters a filthy oath. On the replay Sven slaps a thigh really quite hard, and mouths something like "Oh Gosh!" before leaving to work on another devilishly cunning plan to unleash on the unsuspecting public in the next game – something involving Phil Neville and an early flight home. Sitting in the corner of an emptying but whine-filled bar, I try to remind myself that I'm not bothered. But I can't be bothered.

I find myself taking to the Guinness again. Talking to it, or through it as the case may be. As the bitter liquorice bites, I reflect that The Swede has turned out to be no better than the English British Bulldogs who had the job before him. The saddest thing is, he's no worse either.

The Pubs by Helen Morrison

The pubs will be quieter now
and there'll be no more spontaneous
salutations on the street
until next time. The decorations
are in the bargain bin,
pictures are put away,
until next time.

It doesn't do to be out of synch with the calendar
but of course there may be no next time
for some members of this holy family.
Age or changing fortunes
may rob them of second chances/a second coming.
A temporary exaltation/beatification
is the best most can hope for
and those same followers
who, in their red and white best,
yelled a welcome and lifted their hands
to the coming kings
will return to creosoting the shed.

How much is that clubby in the window?

by Ian Fergus

How does someone buy a football club? I mean you don't simply pick up the phone and ask them straight out, 'How much do you want for it?' It just doesn't happen like that does it?

No, not in a million years.

Yet on a planet far, far away but uncannily like our own, the following telephone calls recently took place.

Call 1

- Is that yourself there, Mark?

      - It certainly is, Liam.

- It's Liam here.

      - It certainly is, Liam. What can I do for you?

- You can meet me at seven for a start and you can get me a drink in, for sure oive a powerful tirst on me so oi have.

      - I think you will find it is your round my friend.

- Who cares whose round it is when the football club we love more than annythin has gone into foinancial meltdown? Do you remember when we were good?

      - I'm afraid I do.

- Nuttin to be afraid of Mark me auld mucker. Oive had a great oidea.

(Which led, after a good few drinks, of course, to the following parallel-world conversation.)

Call 2

- Hello, this is Luuds Uneeted.

    - Oh, hello...I'm er ringing to see how much it would cost erm, to buy your club. Don't hang up, I'm serious.

- I'm not hanging up

    - Oh, good.

- Who are you please?

    - Erm, well my name's Mark. Dyuwantmasurname?

- Well, Mr Dyuwantmasurname, Mr Beech is out just now. Could you call back later?

    - Of course. I'll do that. Bye.

(Mark could not believe how respectfully the receptionist had treated him. In the old days at Luuds, everyone was treated like shut.)

Call 3

- Liam? Hi, it's Mark.

    - Hiya Mark, what did Luuds Uneeted say?

- Well, they didn't say no. Shows how desperate they are.

    - It does. Oi told you it was worth a call. You said it

92

was crazy just to ring and ask to buy 'em. Oi said it was worth it did oi not?

- But what if they now say yes? We've no money. I thought it was only pub talk.

- Don't worry. Remember that guy oi know back in Oirland, the one who put on the Yurovision Snog Contest. He's rolling in it.

- Yeh, Donal isn't it? But is he daft enough to pour millions of pounds into a huge hole just to bail out a Ninglish football club?

- Moight be.

(The next day, for in that distant world, they too have days.)

Call 4

- Hello, Luuds Uneeted.

- Oh, hi, this is Mark here. Is Mr Beech in yet?

- Yes he is and he will see you. Could you possibly call in tomorrow?

- Well, I think so. I'd like to bring my mate, Liam. Ok?

- That will be fine. Can you come to the Yeast Stand at 5.00?

- We'll be there.

(This call proves it is on a planet far, far away because nothing like this could possibly happen in the world football fans know here.)

Call 5

- Donal? Hi. It's Liam, to be sure. We've had our little talk with Trover Beech.

    - Roight. How was he? Could you trust him?

- Oi reckon so. Tink he's a straight dealer. Funny, though. He wanted to make sure Prefosser Ser Join Maparty didn't know about tings. Said he'd only get in the way.

    - So when do you get to see the books?

- Next week. Just in toim for Christmas. Be quite a Christmas present for Luuds fans, Donal.

    - Could be. Sure you can call me then.

- Shall do.

(It's worth noting that Donal, Mr Yurovision, always plays it cool. He's the dark character that makes the parallel world three dimensional.)

Call 6

- Is that yerself Donal? Liam, here.

    - It's Donal myself, sure. How'd it go?

- Er, ok and then again.

    - Go on.

- Well, Trover Beech was upfront. Said we could have the lot for only £40 million.

    - Did you see the books?

- We saw the books, bijaeb. You wouldn't believe what some guys are getting for doing sweet FA. And Pewter Roadsale had been shelling out hundreds just for a tankful of piranha fish.

    - You're making me nervous.

- Oi'm just being honest. There won't be any of that nonsense with Beech in charge and Maparty out the way.

    - What's in it for me, Liam?

- You get the glory of saving a footie club that has a worldwoide name.

    - Well, it's true that everybody has heard of Luuds Uneeted but oi'm tinkin it's just too big a risk, you know. There's got to be some profit in it for me somewhere. Oi'm sorry.

- Oi reckon you're right Donal me auld pal. Pity, though.

    - Sure, tis.

(This is where credibility has been stretched to the limit about such a crazy world. Incompetent, greedy bunglers in charge of something precious to tens of thousands? Highly improbable, it is agreed.)

Call 7

- Liam!

    - It's yerself, Mark.

- If I don't see you, have a Happy Christmas. Hey, you won't believe this but I'm outside a pub here in Luuds city centre and I can see Pewter Roadsale walking towards me - in a chuffing monkey suit.

- You don't say.

- It's true.

- Sums him up so it does.

- What did Donal say?

- Sorry, pal. Nuttin doin. Too much of a risk.

- Aw, what a pity. Wish we could have done it, for all the Luuds fans.

- You're roight, to be sure.

(Monkey suited ex-chairmen is where the story might tip over the edge into the ludicrous except that the parallel world lacks some of the advantages of our world full of heroes.)

Call 8

- Daarr-ling?

- Mark, you're drunk.

- Might be. Said I'd ring yoooo.

- Thanks for the thought. That's what girlfriends are for. Well, how did it go?

- No deal I'm afraid. They're bustards.

- Who are?

- All of them. They're all a set of bustards. An I wanted to do it for Gnawman and Bully and Dan Ruvie and Snuffer. I still love them all and I love all the fans and I love yoooo. The bustards.

- Are you on the train?

- Yam. People are all looking funny at me but I don't care. It's Christmas and I love Luuds Uneeted and they're all bustards.

- Come home. Quick. And shut up.

- Oh sure, I'll do that. Byeeee!

(What a scary world. Thank goodness nothing like that could ever happen in our world!)

Football would become an even greater game if someone invented a ball that kicks back

Eric Morecambe

The Marked Man

by James Lee

James Hill is anxious but focussed. Oblivious to the hubbub of
the converging crowd, he listens only to the stop-start ratchet of the
clunking turnstile, focussing his eyes on the large white number ten
on the blue shirt of the man before him in the shuffling queue. His
elderly heart pumps with a fast, shallow beat and he keeps forgetting
to exhale, his breath unintentionally held, like a child in a wardrobe
hiding from his seeker. With his left thumb and forefinger, he
pinches his nose clean. This unnecessary attention to his already
whistle-clean snout bears testament to his nervousness and, by
extension, his guilt, for in his right hand Hill is carrying a rolled up
cloth banner – a banner with a dangerously dissenting message.

At that very same moment Damon Gilhouly is intently belting a
match ball against a featureless wall in a wide, harshly lit corridor
deep inside the stadium. The eye-blinking slap of leather on painted
breezeblock and its distorted swirling echo is irritating to the bibbed
stewards, but Gilhouly is single-minded in his pre-match routine. He
squirts isotonic drink from a logo-ed squeezy bottle to wet his dry
mouth, spits it out like a between-rounds boxer, then slams another
right-left-right combination.

With the turnstile clunking and the match ball slamming, one of
the Corporation's marksmen takes up his position on the very lip of

the bagel-shaped roof. This elevated vantage point offers clear views of the pitch and three of the four stands. He adopts the low prone position, lying on his front and propping himself with his elbows. An accomplished assassin, he begins to breathe deeply, coaxing his heart to a slow regular thud. He cradles his rifle. With his head motionless, he gently closes his left eye and peers with his right through the telescopic sight of his gun. He dispassionately surveys the red dot of his laser-targeting device as it traces a random path over an advert for health insurance.

By now Hill has reached the turnstile. Though still nervous, he has overcome his fidgeting and holds his banner before him, proudly, like a ceremonial staff. Such paraphernalia are not banned, although the literary content of his certainly is, but they are hugely outdated and could invite snooping for concealed weapons. Surely they won't suspect an old man, Hill hopes. Affecting the self-possessed demeanour of a distinguished elder, he presents his pass to the inscrutable steward. He blows into the breathalyser, presses his thumb against the laser pad and, with his head held high, looks into the cornea scanner. His sobriety and biometric data verified, Hill takes his pack of Bio-Patches from the counter, bids a firm "Thank you" to the turnkey and pushes against the worn bars. One last ratchet of the anachronistic turnstiles and he's in, banner un-checked and in hand. He visits the toilet, then takes up his seat and awards himself a half-smile. Hill's mission is half complete.

Not far away, Gilhouly is also ready. In two restless rows, the teams line up in the tunnel. Some players engage in banter to lighten the mood, others stay silent, maintaining their intensity. A few stretch off tight hamstrings or roll tense shoulders, while others make final adjustments to their hair. Gilhouly, always contemptuous of such preening, is poker-faced and ominously calm. His body language speaks of utter confidence and clarity of purpose. Among these powerful impressive men Gilhouly is the alpha-male. Although just a boy, he is the one player everyone senses. He seems to grow taller and broader each passing moment. An official gives the signal and the ref leads the teams out onto the pitch. Gilhouly hears the tumultuous roar of the crowd, he smells the smoke of the flares and he feels the heat of the sun through his blue number ten shirt. The carpet becomes turf; he crosses his chest and sprints towards his adoring fans.

The height of a goalie's punt above the pitch, the marksman, with his crow's nest's view, begins to scan his target area. The pressure of the hard galvanised roof beneath his elbows is already transmitting up through his upper arms to his shoulder sockets, straining them. He tries not to think of the ache, which will become a pain, and instead adjusts his earpiece. Real-time radio contact with Surveillance and Security is essential if he, and the other sharpshooters, are to pick off trouble causers. Actually, now that news of this fly swatter justice has spread, the number of completed hits has decreased; a tell tale red dot about the sternum usually being enough to dissuade would-be hooligans or dissidents. Once targeted, they either freeze in breathless terror awaiting the bullet that the laser may or may not forewarn, or else they dance a curious jig as if evading an especially fearsome and persistent wasp. Whether called upon or not, each gunman must be absolutely prepared.

With kick-off just minutes away, the entire crowd is sat, as they should be. Over the speakers the command is given to attach Bio-Patches and 50,000 fans open their packs. In unison with the multitude, Hill takes Sensor No1, peels back the tape that masks the adhesive and sticks it on his right temple. Dutifully he continues this routine. He sticks No2 to his left palm and No3 to his throat. In short order each supporter has become a Feedbacker and from then on real-time readings of palm moisture, voice volume, pulse rate and brain activity are beamed from 50,000 pocket transponders to a central receiver in the TV Producer's Gallery. Banks of monitors there begin to flash and bleep as live biometric data sorted by demographic group is displayed. Like anaesthetists scrutinising the vital signs of a super-organism, the production team can now analyse crowd responses to events on the pitch.

And so, with Hill ready to unfurl his dissenting banner, Gilhouly set for glory, and with the marksman fingering his trigger, the ref puts the whistle to his lips, blows hard and the ninety minutes begin. Only one of the participants knows exactly how events will unfold.

Hill barely notices kick-off. He has always been disturbed by the Bio-Patch / Feedbacker business and now he indulges in a daydream of resentment and nostalgia. Besides the obvious mild discomfort of wearing the sensors, he is sure that Corporation claims that their Feedbacking enhances customer satisfaction are disingenuous. It is common knowledge that information so gathered not only results in tighter shorts and funkier hairstyles but also in the brutal discarding of unfancied players. He has also learned that throat patches detect more than just volume of cheering; conversational content is also monitored. Apparently "Come with me, Sir" invitations at half time and door knocks in the early hours are more than urban myths. Sat with his banner, he is determined not to say anything for fear of receiving a tap on the shoulder. He doesn't want to attract attention, not yet anyway.

Instead he delves deep into his memories. Few people remember anything pre-Davidovich, but Hill is one of them. He attended old Division One matches as a boy and Premiership matches in his twenties. Now retired and nearly eighty, his mind plays him a home movie of memories. There's no decay in the celluloid, no flicker or fuzz; the images in this mental film are crystal clear and, as far as he remembers, accurate. His mind settles on Paul Gascoigne, with his pranks, his tears and his sublime skill. He sighs at the pathetic circus act Gazza became, but then smiles at the Scotland goal and the Dentist's Chair. He remembers such icons and their adventures as clearly as other more recent events he would rather forget, because, to Hill, football in 2048 is quite simply mad.

For a kick off, none of the old clubs are left; no Notts County, no Preston North End and no Crewe Alexandra – famous names, each long since perished. Arsenal and Liverpool proved more durable than most, but both met the same end. Newcastle and Sunderland prevailed for a time, but only after merging in undignified futility. Even Manchester United, the strongest of brands with the most customers, is no more. On 6th February 2038, eighty years after the Munich Air Disaster and ten years ago from today, this last English club, but one, was taken over by Davidovich – multi-billionaire media mogul, Milan Davidovich.

Hill resents, even now, that clubs surrendered so quickly, their shareholders so eager to trade identity for riches. Some clubs, sympathetic to the wishes of the fans, acquiesced with reluctance to the Blue Menace. A few chairmen and their boards, at least, required considerable persuasion, both financial and emotional, but the outcome was the same. Hill watched as all across the continent the same story unfolded. Team by team European football was dismantled, or united, as Davidovich bragged. In "The Harvest" the clubs were at first cherry-picked and later scythed until finally, when Man U offered up her fruits, Chelsea became and is to this day the only football club in Europe; monolithic Mother Chelsea.

Obviously a team needs an opposition, and for the past decade Chelsea have played the only other team on the planet, Beijing Guoan – the other half of Davidovich's master plan and not a name Hill had grown up with. In the 30s, the burgeoning Chinese League fell just like those in Europe, and Beijing now serves as the repository of all non-European football talent. US Soccer clubs sold out in a New York minute as their players learned Mandarin and practiced chopsticks on their French fries. Latino and African teams, publicly indignant but laughably corrupt behind the scenes, fell over themselves in the gold rush. The remaining Australasian teams boarded this team bus like the podgy last child out of the changing rooms – still damp from the showers and anxious not to be left behind.

The twisted logic of Davidovich's World League was clear to Hill; two-club cities had more fans than those with one - the choice was which to follow, not whether – and so by extension a world with two teams would have more fans, and hence more revenue. Committed fans were happy to encourage the less zealous and, in this atmosphere of obligation, fan-base and coffers swelled.

Despite this Chelsea-Beijing duopoly, thousands still play professional football, but they are nursery or finishing school footballers. In England, for example, they whore themselves twice weekly for Chelsea United or Chelsea Town, The Shed Albion or Lampard Wanderers. Whatever their name, these feeder clubs exist only to benefit Chelsea. They scout, train, and mould the nation's best, punching out players, like struck medals or minted coins – all at Chelsea's behest.

Hill sees both poetry and pretence in such names. "The Bridge Argyle" sounds better than "Chelsea SW Region, Academy No 4", but he feels the descriptive nature of the latter at least holds no deception. For all the poetry of Blue Hotspur there's little honesty. Such tinges of tradition are illusory for in the Football of 2048 there is no history.

Once, Hill saw Stamford County take on Terry Forest, and it felt like an East Midlands derby, but it was a charade. County's veteran

Goalie had a Rams tattoo and aged City Grounders brandished foam oak trees, but such tokenism was and is pitiful; only Chelsea matters. The dwindling few, like Hill, who remember when Chelsea was just another team, are a dying breed.

So, this afternoon, like every afternoon, Chelsea will play Beijing - it will be the second of their four daily games. Four times every day they face each other, from the end of August until May – a thousand games a season. With the build-up and the analysis, the match, as it were, is almost continuous. A pronounced squad rotation system within the two armies of players is used, but even so the two managers (Davidovich's sons) struggle to balance the conflicts between the need for three points, star player exposure and physical recovery. Hill once met the two juniors and he isn't surprised that they struggle.

Geography too is a consideration. With fans worldwide and Chelsea and Beijing teams in every country, each day brings matches in Chicago or Kyoto, Mumbai or wherever. Episodic use of stadiums in ever-westward time zones ensures that kick-off is always at 3pm, ground time. But this scheduling is not for reasons of nostalgia. With fossil fuels almost gone, the fact is that daylight play averts the need for floodlights. Hill misses the vivid, glistening green of floodlit pitches on icy nights and the X-shaped shadows of players in luminous strip. For him, evening games had more immediacy, a kind of hyper-reality.

In fact, the modern game holds little charm for Hill. He knows the organisers make it seem spectacular, with Rock music and pretty girls in the west and kite flying and beheadings in the east, but the actual matches are quite dull. With so many goals, usually from long range or choreographed to be volleyed by bicycle-kick, it's hard for purists like him to get excited at all. Luckily for Davidovich Corporation, cognoscenti are as rare as the true footballers they crave and the ignorant crowds instead delight in their fast-food diet of bizarre goal celebrations and pantomime punch-ups.

The greatest source of disenchantment for Hill is the players of 2048. Although he is appalled, and a little amused, by their ridiculous modish hairstyles and vulgar tattoos, he concedes it is not for him to judge their appearance, fashion being an accoutrement of youth. But he believes he is justified, entitled even, to criticise the way they play. To him these obviously impressive athletes, with all their fancy tricks, personify the triumph of style over content. Compared to Platini, Cantona or Zidane, they have little intelligence.

For all their showboating, they know nothing of the artistry of previous ages and need none of the desire or courage that was essential then. Like ball-juggling idiot pop-stars they strut and they pose, they lunge and they flail, craving attention with each melodramatic gesture. Nowadays all players are like this, all except one.

Hill has come to despise football. He still cherishes its possibilities and can wax lyrical over the defining moments in its long history, but he regards the football of his retirement years as an intricate illusion. For all its glamour and supposed importance it is fake, entirely commercial and the plaything and vehicle of a tyrant. Of course it's something of a cliché for wistful old has-beens to claim that the past was rosier, but he knows the reality behind the public's understanding. He knows because, to his profound regret, Hill worked for Davidovich and so helped to impose his tyranny.

With ten minutes on the clock, the two teams are still sizing each other up. The action, for want of a better word, has involved neat and tidy, almost polite, approach work; three times ending with an offside flag and twice with an over-hit through ball. Barely a foul has been committed, never mind a corner won or a shot struck, making this a typically cagey, actually rather dull, opening passage of play.

Hill is facing the Stamford Bridge pitch but, in the absence of incident, he is still daydreaming. Eventually his reminiscences dry up and he becomes aware of his wider surroundings. In the centre circle a skilful shimmy away from a tackle and a deft pass into space brings the first applause of the day, and with it his first conscious sighting of Gilhouly, the one player he admires. Awoken from his reverie and feeling insignificant in the vast crowd, the enormity of his task dawns on him.

He begins to question the wisdom of making a protest at all; of buying two broom handles, a tin of gloss paint and a 5cm brush, and of ruining a perfectly good cream duvet cover. Last night as he spread and stapled his canvas and daubed his message in dangerous red, there was no doubt in his mind. But now, with the difficult task of getting the banner into the ground done and finding himself on the brink of a noble deed, Hill feels his resolve weakening. With the inherent risk of injury from baton or bullet, and with his action seeming unlikely to trouble Davidovich Corporation at all, this could be folly.

The DC hierarchy take a dim view of betrayal and, retired or not, Hill cannot escape the fact that he was one of them. In the early 2000s, around the time Davidovich bought Chelsea, Hill hung up for good his journeyman's football boots and took up writing. Always more comfortable on the periphery looking in, he relished at once the act of putting into words his observations and his thoughts. At first he traded off his lower league reputation, using his contacts to gain interviews and writing match reports with an insider's perspective. Before long he graduated from freelancer to local rag hack, and thence to the nationals – a meteoric rise for a self-educated ex-semi-pro, a rise that would ultimately take him to DC's InfoMinistry.

While there, editing the TV News and scripting the ad libs for the hapless anchormen, Hill maintained the demeanour of a Corporation Man, utterly committed to the Davidovich cause. That he pulled it off was quite a feat as privately Hill disbelieved the very propaganda he was required to write.

But Comrade Hill wasn't some Trojan horse hero, bent on destroying the enemy from within. His second divorce had cleaned him out and he needed the money, and being in the injury time of his career he towed the Corporation line. The big man himself had read a piece Hill had written on how football could save teenagers from crime. Davidovich liked that Hill entertained such notions as right and wrong, that his morality was black and white (it was in the article). He felt Hill had potential, despite his advancing years, and that he might, with guidance, be of some use in his crusade to instil fear in the masses and sell football shirts. So Hill sold out.

At the InfoMinistry, he witnessed first hand the evil machinations of the Davidovich regime. They say evil prospers if good men do nothing, and Hill is certainly guilty of inaction. But in truth he did more than nothing, one could say he was an accomplice. At first, Hill had convinced himself he was simply writing copy, but in time this delusion lifted and clarity dawned. He grew to hate Davidovich the man and Chelsea the ideology. Mostly, Hill grew to hate himself for doing his bidding and for taking his blood money.

Eventually and with blessed relief, Hill retired, receiving a "Life" Season Ticket to watch Chelsea. Not "The Shed Albion" or "Lampard Wanderers", but bona fide Chelsea, the real deal. Like a gold watch, this privilege was gifted him after ten years in the employ of Davidovich – "Presented with esteem and gratitude to Comrade James Hill on the occasion ..." etc. etc. Hill accepted this pat on the back with good grace and he tried to enjoy the matches, despite the taint of guilt.

Over the years this guilt stayed with Hill, nagging his conscience like a mental blister. The redemptive strike, for which he is now poised, should close the book on his guilt, and on another more recent and more concrete concern, but he is scared. As if to seal Hill's misgivings, a single gunshot echoes around the ground. A careless individual in the fifty thousand crowd must have made a loose dissenting comment, no doubt inspired by Gilhouly, without first removing their throat Bio-Patch - a rudimentary mistake by a most foolhardy Feedbacker. Hill is not surprised. Usually Surveillance and Security let mild anti-Davidovich rhetoric go but in the increasingly rebellious climate palpable since the advent of Gilhouly, the authorities have clearly decided to send a chastening reminder to would-be dissenters. This particular dissenter receives his reminder from one of the rooftop marksmen, and it enters his consciousness through his right shoulder.

A mixture of shock, indignation and gallows humour spreads through the crowd. From his seat close to the touchline and almost level with half way, Hill can see the ensuing melee behind the Chelsea goal. Medics are escorting the loose-tongued casualty away for treatment as Stewards restore order with palm wafting "sit down" gestures. Hill is far from reassured by the crude medical attention and the mollifying actions of the otherwise pit bull-like Stewards. His mind is once more in turmoil and he shakes with fear. Hill is almost sunk by this shot-across-the-bows.

He knows he should abort his possibly fatal and probably futile mission; he should keep his banner furled, watch the match from the stands, forgo the hospitality and leave before the final whistle. But Hill, not being one to shirk his responsibilities knows this is not an option; pride alone dictates he must finish what he's started. In any case, it's only a matter of time before someone not party to his intensions takes an interest in the bundle of cloth and two poles that rest by his side. Hill knows he must warn Gilhouly, whatever the consequences – he is too important to lose, and with the Corporation clearly threatened by Gilhouly, losing him is a distinct possibility. If guilt sensitises Hill, then Gilhouly's current plight compels him to act.

It is hard to overstate the profound influence Gilhouly has had on Hill. Since he retired in '38, Hill has attended Stamford Bridge twice monthly. Until the advent of the lad there wasn't much to get excited about, but being an ex-employee he is well looked after and there are always old colleagues around with interesting gossip to pass on.

From time to time Hill imagines he's watching a game from the distant past - Euro 2000, Italia '90 even. Like many of his age Hill has a memory that is archaeological in its offerings and surprising in its clarity. And so on occasions when he finds himself absorbed in the action, he substitutes in his mind the contemporary players for latter-day greats. One moment the Beijing right back is tearing down the wing to cross and the next Alan Shearer is rising to bury the header. Such moments though, are rare. Then last year, on a bright cold day in April, it happened - an event so startling, miraculous even, that Hill felt something inside him reawaken. Nearly 80 years old and he rediscovered the thrill - the joyful, soaring thrill - of watching a truly great footballer play with total freedom and without fear. Hill had witnessed for the first time the precocious genius of Chelsea's Damon Gilhouly.

Everything he did and does reminds Hill of a Great. Receiving the ball on the edge of the box, in an instant he is Gazza, twinkle-toed and quick-thinking, hop-scotching through tackles, threading tramline passes between defenders. Then, charging from deep, he is Maradona; barrel-chested and beefy with the balance of a skate boarder and the close control of a hockey player.

Gilhouly is only a teenager, a boy really, but he has the physique of a man, and a manly man at that. He doesn't run, he bounds. Opponents are skittled as he bounces through them like a rubber bowling ball or a Barnes-Wallis bomb. Bursting with muscle and brimming with hormones, he is charismatic in his physicality – Hill can't take his eyes off him. Most importantly, Hill feels reborn by Gilhouly's very existence; he's so young and uncorrupted. Just knowing he exists offers Hill a kind of salvation.

A few seasons ago, Hill recalls, there was something complimentary written about a precocious Merseyside schoolboy from a Celtic family. Surely the schoolboy was Gilhouly and certainly the reports were prophetic; Gilhouly is a prodigy.

There have been, Hill remembers, many talented youngsters before. Every other year some skinny teenager strings two or three half-decent performances together and they're presented by the media as mini-messiahs. Self-justifying pundits, ever eager to appear sage, then to board the praise train, issue hosannas and prophesy greatness. Before you know it, the object of their adulation is burnt out or injured, or else his tricks have been demystified and his effectiveness blunted, by which time the next next-big-thing is teed up. Hill was not without complicity in this regard.

After a year, a long time in today's accelerated schedule, Gilhouly's effectiveness is far from blunted. No amount of analysis by the Beijing coaching staff nor any degree of effort on the part of their players can counter his irrepressible talent. The best opponents can hope for is to starve him of service, stifle his brilliance and dampen his spirit. And yet, for all their endeavour and strategy, "Demon Damon" usually prevails, much to Hill's delight.

Statistically, as anoraks will tell you, his record is very impressive, and very skewed. On the plus side, Gilhouly always rates well at the Davidovich Monthly Football Awards, which Hill obviously loathes. For example, last month he achieved a near clean sweep of gongs for which he was eligible; Most Shots on Target, Highest Goal-to-Shot Ratio, Top Scorer and Most Assists. Only in Most Free Kicks Netted did he miss out, coming Runner-Up to Galactico Beckham, grandson of the sainted David. On the negative side however, although not to Hill, is Gilhouly's indifference to fashion and his refusal to engage in histrionics or the melodramatic. Indeed, he cares little for pretension or ceremony and regards clothing as a means of preventing nudity. He therefore features prominently in polls for Worst Dressed Man and never at all in Best Goal Celebration. These days, more and more fuss is made of such peripherals and as a result genuine football pundits are now only equal billing, at best, with style gurus and fashion critics. In fact, on that April afternoon at Stamford Bridge, the only thing more astonishing to Hill than his first glimpse of Gilhouly making his debut was the crowd's initial silence at his obvious brilliance. They didn't know what to make of him and what they saw as his old-fashioned, no-thrills style of play. This brow-furrowing bemusement soon gave way to eye-widening disbelief, for it was only a matter of time before he scored and his squashed, pasty face was flashed on the giant screen. Unique among the footballers of 2048, Damon is not a handsome man.

On arriving at Chelsea from his feeder club, Stanley Park Blues, this posed something of a challenge to the commentators and the ad men. Used to working with the elegant, the stylish and the beautiful, they now had to promote this bland dumpy boy with sticky-out ears. Gilhouly's position was therefore quite precarious and twice he was almost dropped. Until the masses forgave his aesthetic inadequacies and learned to appreciate his footballing genius, Gilhouly was both enigmatic and endangered.

Luckily for him and for football, sufficient people of influence within Davidovich Corp could see his genuine talent and his future merchandising potential and so Chelsea persevered. Before long his approval rating crept up and then soared and this previously one-dimensional misfit became a multi-faceted hero. Today, to quote the graffiti, 'Gilhouly is God.'

Just as he awoke something within Hill, an old-timer who'd known football pre-Davidovich, so too Gilhouly stirs people too young to remember anything other than the current circus. It is as if some primeval instinct or some dormant aspect of human nature is aroused by his free-spiritedness and his fearlessness. The Corporation, usually so reactionary, so wary of upsetting the apple cart, did not foresee this threat to their establishment.

For too long fans have experienced, with frazzled senses and corrupted understanding, a game whose raison d'etre was to unite the people in vague insecurity, fear, and hatred of an unknown enemy, and to generate revenue. To Hill, this is football devoid of humanity. Gilhouly now provides this humanity. With his fearlessness and his disregard for hollow conventions, he shows people their possibilities. They need not live in a climate of fear and frivolity, violence and vanity. This is the truth and the truth can set them free. Or, as fans might more succinctly put it: Gil-houly! Gil-houly! Gil-houly!

That he should become popular was inevitable and not a problem for DC; that his popularity usurped Chelsea's was. At first this idol worship of an individual embarrassed Davidovich's Top Brass. Surely it was they who should manipulate the emotions of the crowd, not some unconventional, dangerously free-willed teenager. Less love of Gilhouly and more hatred of the opposition, that's what the Corporation wanted.

It was hoped that with so many games worldwide Gilhouly's influence would be localised and diluted. But his fame spread, and crowds in stadiums never featuring Gilhouly chanted his name. DC sought therefore to discredit him, publishing stories of his weakness for junk food and prostitutes. This only widened his popularity and many, like Hill, doubted the validity of such claims anyway. Also, formerly dependable team mates, and even opponents, began adopting his less-sizzle-more-sausage style of play. They might not possess his unique talents, but they could certainly abandon the pantomime and concentrate on the purer drama of football itself.

This stirred hope in Hill, whose fatherly love for Gilhouly had become devotional.

Today, with Gilhouly's influence spreading, DC is seriously worried. Their wunderkind has become a fomenter of dissent; his is the spark that might lead to unrest and then downwards to protest, rebellion and even to revolution. It is probably too late to nip him in the bud and it will be difficult not to make a martyr of him, but, with the status quo so profoundly under threat, Gilhouly's days are numbered.

In his heart, Hill knows this. He knows the ruthlessness of DC and is sure that Gilhouly, an obvious loose canon, has probably lit the fuse of his own destruction. But Hill's imminent protest at Stamford Bridge will not be directed at the object of his enmity; Milan Davidovich is long dead and to attack the faceless corporation he bequeathed the world would be an act of futility. Instead, Hill's banner will address an individual and, in actuality, it will be less a protest and more a warning; "GILHOULY: THEY ARE GOING TO KILL YOU!" it will read.

Hill remains nervous from the shooting. To calm himself he recalls the snippets of insider information leaked to him by concerned ex-colleagues still at the InfoMinistry. Once Hill had intimated his worries for Gilhouly to just one of his older workmates, he was virtually spoon-fed evidence. Like-minded people, employees he barely knew, and even strangers, began sidling up to him in hospitality or at the in-ground betting outlets. Almost with a nod and a wink they'd engage him in cautious conversation, insinuating their own similar fears and expressing solidarity with his cause (he hadn't yet realised he had "a cause"). The details they fed him – the high level resignations, the increased surveillance of Gilhouly, the plans to pay him off, the plots to do him in – now played out in Hill's thoughts. They are going to kill Gilhouly, he concluded.

This restores Hill's sense of purpose. He knows he is right and he knows he must act. Also, where before he felt anonymous and lost in a crowd of strangers, his recollections of encouragement and collusion have evoked in him a sense of togetherness. He may be acting alone, but he will be a conduit for the sentiments of many. Through him the crowd will warn; "GILHOULY - THEY ARE GOING TO KILL YOU!"

Hill is almost ready, but one niggling doubt remains; will it work? How can a painted bed sheet on two sticks have any effect? He consoles himself with the thought that, in one respect, he can't fail. He has carried with him for years the guilt of complicity with Davidovich. His time at the InfoMinistry is the one stain on his professional reputation and the dark regret that sinks him to sleep at night. Hill is an old man, enjoying an Indian summer of sprightliness, but he knows his body and mind will fade. Now, with his faculties still mostly intact, he has a chance to settle his accounts with dignity. Precisely because of the risk of injury, or worse, this will be an act of contrition and redemption.

Serenity suffuses Hill. He knows his evidence is reliable, his suspicions well founded and his intensions justified. Like a barrister summing up his case for the defence of Gilhouly, Hill has swayed the jury of his mind. He is confident now that his action will work; far from futile, it is necessary and bound to succeed, and he has the fans behind him. His chest swells, a nodding smile softens his face and he pats his banner with pride. Hill now focuses all his attention on the pitch and waits for his moment in history.

Play is approaching the half-hour mark and, with the phoney war of the first ten minutes over, the match is starting to simmer. Gilhouly, of course, has looked lively, but close chaperoning by his markers has thwarted his courtship of the ball thus far. Beijing Guoan have the upper hand. The Nigerian-Chinese axis of Amaku and Wong are bossing midfield and Mo Khan has got the better of Leblanc, skinning the Chelsea left-back seemingly at will. On 31 minutes, Khan floats past the Frenchman delivering a precision cross onto the forehead of American Taz Kowolski, whose bullet header is tipped onto the crossbar and over for a corner. Despite Beijing's dominance the game is still goalless and the home crowd are tense rather than overtly worried.

With a thousand games a season the title is usually still in the balance at the end of April. Such a marathon programme stands comparison with the 400km stages of the earliest Tours de France or the six months it used to take the England Cricket Team to play an Ashes Series down under. Therefore, a losing streak of, say, four or five games is incidental in today's mammoth season. Beijing, however, have not won now for nineteen matches, the best part of a week, and so Hill is quite pleased to see them in today's match enjoying a modicum of possession, exerting pressure and thereby spicing up the contest. This old fashioned enjoyment of challenge and competition and being uncertain of the result is at odds with the choreographed hard-nosed nastiness of the current game.

On 39 minutes a wilfully injurious tackle halts proceedings on the pitch. To Hill's right, Leblanc was breaking out of defence down Chelsea's left flank, approaching at a sprint. As he crossed halfway, Amaku, Beijing's enforcer, cruelly chopped him down, bang in front of the dugouts and just yards from Hill. Now, predictably, a fracas is in progress. Third-party players exchange "afters" in solidarity with their either aggrieved or innocent team mate, and tracksuited coaching staff exchange words.

For several minutes the ref struggles to restore order and only does so with a pair of red cards – one to Amaku for the initial reckless challenge and the other to Chelsea's Winston for remonstrating in similarly reckless fashion. Eventually, Beijing retreat and Gilhouly stands over the ball waiting for the necessary substitution, planning the free kick he will float into the box. But play cannot resume as Leblanc is still flat out. Not having responded to the magic spray, he is clearly seriously injured and is slowly being scooped up to be laid on a stretcher.

Gilhouly, impassive and with arms akimbo, is no more than fifteen metres away from Hill. It has been a strangely anonymous performance for someone usually so influential. Standing motionless in this eerie transitional episode of the game Gilhouly appears ordinary, vulnerable even. With action suspended and no superhuman feats to admire, it is easy to see the boy in him and not the messiah figure for whom Hill plans to risk everything. But Hill, having resolved to banish emotion from his mind, is immune to such re-evaluation. He is convinced of Gilhouly's status and is bent on a single course of action.

It is now more than six minutes since play was interrupted and with the quiet crowd still awaiting Leblanc's removal and replacement the atmosphere has gone flat. Far off sounds – a police siren, a squeal of bus brakes – can be heard coming in and then out of earshot in the light breeze. Within the ground, occasional shouts of 'Get on with it!' and the like, punctuate the quiet. Hill is restless for an entirely different reason and grips his banner tightly, steeling himself to rise.

With play suspended and Gilhouly so close, Hill knows he won't get a better chance. Also with Leblanc nearly off the pitch and the sub, Schmidt, almost stripped, the clock is ticking. So, Hill braces himself to warn Gilhouly now, this very moment. Using his banner like a ski pole he pulls himself to his feet.

Having sat for the best part of an hour, his unsteady legs feel bloodless and unresponsive. He shuffles the short sideways journey to his left, his banner knocking into seated fans on the row below him. At the steps, liberated from the physical constraints of communal supporting, he sees that there is not a single steward between him and the pitch; amazingly he has a clear run with no one to intervene. At first gingerly but gathering pace under gravity, he descends with a stamp-stamp-tap, the poles of his banner making a tripod of his rickety frame and supplying a metronome to the rhythm of his descent. In barely ten strides he is pitch side.

Hill is breathless from the exertion and the stress of this unnatural attention seeking. To his surprise, he hears himself shouting hoarsely.

'Damon! Turn round, Damon! Over here!'

But, unused to raising his voice and as good as lacking a diaphragm, his throat tightens and any initial volume quickly fades to a rasping croak. Feeling awkward, his face flushes as he struggles to unravel his banner.

He senses someone next to him and turns to see Moore, an ex-colleague. Moore has taken hold of one of the poles and is helpfully pulling and turning it. With the full message displayed, the two men raise the banner above their heads and Hill, more assuredly this time and with greater urgency, shouts again.

'Damon! Turn round Damon! You must protect yourself – they are going to kill you! THEY ARE GOING TO KILL YOU!'

Moore follows suit.

'Gilhouly! They are going to kill you! Watch your back, Gilhouly!' he bellows with confidence.

With the crowd still hushed from the interruption of the Leblanc injury, the two voices can be heard clearly in the stillish air. Gilhouly can hear them. The odd shout of 'Sitdarn!' directed at Hill, rings out, but so too do other alerting cries.

'Gilhouly! Watch out! Watch your back, Gilhouly!'

Before long there's a chorus.

'WATCH YOUR BACK – HEY! – WATCH YOUR BACK – GIL-HOULY WATCH YOUR BACK!'

A few even leave their seats to join Hill, forming a picket line of alarm and sympathy for Gilhouly. Hill's belief grows, he swells with pride and yells and waves with increasing courage. A feeling of togetherness, of synergy, courses through him. Not in his dreams did he imagine it would go so well, it is like it was choreographed.

Gilhouly is genuinely intrigued by all the commotion and rather puzzled by the sentiment. He knows he shouldn't have bunked training the other day, but why would they want to kill him? He leaves the ball where he's placed it and walks towards Hill. A man of the people, Gilhouly wants to calm their fears and, in truth, his own.

At this point, word is given for the stewards to make their move. Having kept their distance, listening keenly for the "Engage!" command to cut through the radio chatter of their earpieces, they now march over en masse and with purpose.

Likewise the marksman is ordered to take aim. Earlier today, when first he received details of the job, he was a little surprised, considering the age and standing of the victim. He must have asked for it, he thought, dismissing his concern. Now, still lying in a prone shooting position, he trains his laser between the shoulder blades of the target. He concentrates hard, listening for the final confirmation to shoot. From experience he knows that a second shot, fired to atone for a messy first, dents his satisfaction of a job well done and so he is determined to kill cleanly with a single bullet.

By now the crowd too is intrigued, and entertained, and the two teams look on bemused. Gilhouly reaches the gathering. He notices red specks and splashes around the painted words, and sees pepper and salt stubble on Hill's chin. Hill discerns with a smile that Gilhouly has freckles and a faint cast in one eye. Addressing Hill, clearly the foreman, Gilhouly speaks.

'What's the problem?' he says, quite calmly.

Hill lowers his end of the banner and looks right into the eyes of his hero.

Gilhouly feels the warmth.

Hill pauses a while, to compose himself, and then opens his mouth to speak. But, with words of kindness and wisdom emergent on his lips, Hill is bear-hugged and pulled from behind, and the banner is wrenched from his hand. A tide of yellow bibs washes over the few. Punches are thrown and baton swipes connect with elbows and collar bones.

'Easy, fellers!' Gilhouly exclaims to the over-officious stewards, one of who is now bending Hill's frail arm up his back. He jumps over the advertising hoardings to intervene, but two fat attendants block his way.

Hill sees that Gilhouly is trying to help and is pleased, but then cries out in terrible pain as his arm breaks under the steward's pressure.

With Hill neutralised, and the pitch invaders rapidly dispersing, the phrase 'Fire at will!' sounds in the marksman's ear. He exhales, squeezes the trigger until it clicks, and feels a firm jolt to his right shoulder. His ears ring. In an instant chemical energy is transferred to kinetic and a bullet rifles across the stadium towards the red dot that lies in the centre of a large white circle on a blue background.

Hill, being pulled away with the crux of an elbow about his

throat, sees Gilhouly's chest open with a spray of red. He tries to yell out in anguish but the choking forearm stifles all sound. As Gilhouly hits the ground, dead, a crushing realisation flattens Hill. This has been a set up.

The next morning Hill is lying in hospital. A cast protects his pinned and throbbing arm and electrodes on his chest are connected to a machine that goes "beep". No longer a Feedbacker, Hill is now a cardiac patient, having sustained a mild heart attack to go with his broken arm. An orderly lays a newspaper on his bed with mocking gentleness.

'GILHOULY DIES FOR DAVIDOVICH!' declares the front page.

Hill reads the opening paragraph.

'In yesterday's 3pm kick-off a crazed protestor stormed The Bridge just before half time. Ace Damon Gilhouly, seeing that a volunteer steward was being attacked, selflessly jumped to his rescue. Tragically this brave have-a-go-hero and True Blue was killed by accident in the crossfire. Gilhouly died a martyr to the memory of Davidovich. Long live the Corporation.'

Lowering the paper, Hill closes his eyes, empties his lungs and waits for the next shot of morphine.

Star Quality by Helen Morrison

Not beautiful enough for the game apparently
though his game is beautiful.

He's scored goals aplenty
and earned the ovation
and the crazy money.
He's shifted shirts aplenty too
-the obsolete ones going
to the grateful aid agency.

The images that stick
are the mucky jumper
the bubble-gum
the whoring and the gambling

while another player
equally lacking in eloquence
but suave in sunglasses
sometimes even a skirt
has been hailed a king,
that farcical penalty forgotten.

(Nut) Case Histories

"If that's true then it would be a big surprise, but then nothing surprises me in football these days."

Kevin Keegan

Booked!

by Helen Morrison

It's all a mistake! Why am I here again? A football *writers'* group. I thought the notice was advertising a football *reading* group. I don't even like football. All I know about the game comes from sitting with friends, reluctantly, in a pub while they watch matches on the big screen. And my mind always wanders (much like my experience of sermons in earlier life).

I was expecting to tell them all how I'd read *Fever Pitch* because I liked Nick Hornby and how I didn't really enjoy the book - but I never got the chance.

My friend was supposed to be here but I guess she's baled out. I thought this might have appealed to her. She's a podiatrist and, presumably because of her professional interest in feet and legs, had followed the England team around the world. Must have read the advert properly. Like I should have.

I'm not sure what's made me concoct something and come here to The Angel pub. I must be mad. I'm sure it's a mistake but, here goes. What the hell.

Football

I might be envied for my view
of men's legs
and of the sky.
They do look different from my angle...

I can participate fully
without worrying about training diets
nights off the booze
nights off the wife.

I might be envied for the attention
focused on me.
Grown men (well, physically anyway)
can think of little else
as we play out our story.

But think of the blows
from heels or heads,
there's little time to admire the legs
before the pain.

Think of the mud
or worse - the astro turf burn -
I'm sure you'd rather have balls
than be one.

Kes

We can't help but laugh. We can't help but see the clash between the lean energy of that music and the thickened waistline, the thinning hair. Does he really fancy himself a hero as he leaps, head up, knees high, towards the changing room? Have the years convinced him that this anti-team of boys, slim and podgy, nimble and lumbering, each clad in whatever he could find that morning, accord him authority for any reason other than that they are "us" and he is "them"? He promises 'a rare delight' and they borrow team names from the greats, choosing carefully to avoid 'a clash of colours', in his imagination at least (for, of course, they have no colours).

If optimistic we might fancy for a moment that this could offer escape, in the mind at any rate, from the unremitting grey of a life where even the best futures divide into "office" or "manual", or even a genuine alternative, but as we go on we cannot help but see that the cold is biting, they are miserable and this is just one more lesson on the fixed order of things. The scoreline at the bottom of the screen may pretend that they are someone else but they cannot forget who they are. Billy Casper, swathed in borrowed drawers of which the most prudish Victorian might approve, must give up pretending to be a monkey on the goalpost and make at least a pretence of playing his part. This convinces nobody, however, and that long cold shower hammers home the truth.

No more heroes.....

'We've nothing like gladiators any more.'

she said, planting her *Bic* on the desk,
serene in blue and yellow candystripes.
looking forward to secrets shared on the bus home
head filled with soaps and sleepovers

She has never (yet) seen
tier on tier of jeering fans
never (yet) heard
the swearing,
murderous sometimes,
never (yet) felt the shock
as one body crashes into another,
never (yet) hoped
to see one fall as another
runs to victory,
never (yet) noticed
that shops and factories ring
with shouts and vibrate
with shaken fists,
that respectable inexperienced girls
sigh for multiple winners
and streets are filled with blood and wreckage
if victory goes to the wrong side.

Whatsthestory?

(freeze frames)

It could be a dance, a courtly affair. One man looks as if he's come to rest, poised on one knee in the centre. Another, behind him, has right hand and toes raised as if readying to launch into a routine, a jive perhaps. Some fleet pairs trip along side by side, perfectly synchronized, while other couples seem to be frozen mid-Irish-jig. Opposite, a man spins on his back, a breakdancer.

Maybe it's a rite. Other genuflectors have a humble look, hands on thighs, head down, conscious of sin. In happier times, all gaze heavenwards, leap with new purpose, seem to hang there. And alone, with care and deliberation, the corner priests bow low as they place the ball on the ground.

But is it a war? Defeated men clutch heads or try to rise like the dying Gaul or sit abject, shoulders down, legs splayed, stripy Andy Pandies on whom the strings have gone slack.

The Curriculum

Is their eye caught by the Biology
of muscle movement
or the Physics of the flight of the ball?

Are they fascinated by the Art History,
the contrast between flesh and drapery,
the interplay of mass and space?

Or do they consider strategy
with the zest of a general on campaign?

As the game ends, do they envisage piles of laundry
or relish the thought of the slaps on the back?

Is the roar of the crowd meaningless,
merely a foreign language,
or as rousing as a hunting call?

Is this simply an outlet for stress
or a source of philosophical question?

They're different from us, so they say.

Of Gameball and the English Temperament

by Dan McIntyre

> Five days shalt thou labour, as the Bible says. The seventh
> day is the Lord thy God's. The sixth day is for football.
>
> Anthony Burgess

The English had invented a new game, which with characteristic enthusiasm they were as keen on talking about as they were on playing. It was not a particularly sophisticated game, involving as it did two teams of largely drunken people running after a bean-filled leather sack. Neither was the aim of the whole endeavour entirely perspicuous, and such refinements as the number of people allowed on a team and the length of playing time had yet to be finalised. "Gameball", as the pastime had come to be named, was nightly discussed in what served as the tavern for the village, and on this particular occasion the mead was flowing as fast as the conversation with the consequent effect that most of the participants were either well and truly inebriated or well and truly on the way.

'I'm telling you now,' said a large bearded man, jabbing his index finger at the group, 'in that last match I kicked that ball so hard it burst. I reckon I should get a point for that.'

'It's a bloody team game.' came the exasperated reply. 'What's the point in giving you a point individually?'

'And anyway,' said someone else, 'it's a stupid idea to get a point for bursting the ball. We'd have to keep stopping to make a new one.'

There were rumbles of assent and the large bearded man returned to his mead, grumbling to himself.

'I reckon a much better idea is to get a point for kicking the ball into the duck pond.' chipped in another voice.

At this, there were howls of derision. Over the top of this someone shouted, 'How about marking a spot that we have to kick the ball past?'

'That'll never work,' came another voice, 'how'll we know who's kicked the most?'

'We could have two marks,' said a slight, wiry-looking man., 'one for each team. And we could make it somebody's job to count how many times each ball gets kicked past them.'

This suggestion was met with sceptical scowls all round, relying as it did on the intrinsic faith in one person's ability to count. It was at this point that the door of the tavern creaked opened, letting in the biting wind of the winter evening. Standing in the doorway was a cowled figure carrying a large sack. Immediately, the men stopped their conversation and stared in mistrust at the man.

'Good evening, gentlemen.' said the stranger. 'My apologies for interrupting your discussion. I represent Baron Édouard de Beauchamp.'

There was a collective intake of breath. The stranger approached the table of the gameball-obsessed villagers.

'If you will allow me, gentlemen,' he said, 'I should like to put forward a proposition.' At this he undid the drawstring sack and emptied on to the table more silver coins than any of the men had ever seen before.

'If you will agree to my proposal, all of this shall be yours.'

At the sight of the mountain of coins in front of them, the villagers were transfixed. The stranger pushed his hood back and thought that perhaps, just perhaps, his scheme might work.

It was the firm belief of Baron Édouard de Beauchamp that hooliganism ran through the blood of all true-born Englishmen. This, to his consternation, was not a view shared by all of the Norman nobility. Indeed, some of them looked on the native Anglo-Saxons with emotions bordering on the affectionate, and it was even becoming fashionable to claim that as a result of the intermarrying between the Normans and the Saxons that the 1066 invasion had inevitably brought about, it was becoming increasingly difficult to determine what actually constituted a "true-born" Englishman anyway. De Beauchamp, nevertheless, was convinced that a propensity for hostile aggression was a deciding characteristic. His evidence for this position was, to his mind, indisputable. Ever since he had arrived in England and deposed the Saxon baron who had been his predecessor, he had found the English to be surly, rude and utterly uncooperative. It continued to amaze him, for example, that his request for them to supply him with an increased annual turnip crop had not been met with unanimous enthusiasm, especially in light of the extra half a day's holiday a year he was offering in recompense. On the contrary, following his tenants' refusal to accede to his wishes, he had returned home from a hunt one afternoon to find his windows smashed and the main driveway covered in steaming piles of horse manure.

The fact remained that since the ravages of the Black Death the peasants' stock had risen considerably, almost to the point where a baron such as de Beauchamp needed them more than they needed him. This niggled him greatly, and it was fast becoming an unmanageable problem. As Lord of the Manor and tenant-in-chief he relied on those lower down in the hierarchy to keep him in his elevated position. Already the King's men were beginning to bother him for the annual payment he was obliged to make in lieu of his obligation to provide military service to the monarch. Without the help of his knights, vassals, reeves and, ultimately, the army of soil-tillers under them all, it was looking extremely unlikely that he would be able to pay it. And so de Beauchamp found himself faced with a problem that showed no sign of yielding to his usual managerial tactic, which was to ignore it in the hope that it might go away. But as if a problem of that magnitude wasn't enough, there was also the more immediate concern that had been brought to him that morning.

'The peasants want what?' de Beauchamp had asked upon hearing the request for the first time.

Philbert de Vexin, de Beauchamp's occasionally faithful manservant, shuffled uncomfortably, sensing that his master might be about to explode in apoplexy. 'They want an afternoon off, my lord.' he said, all the while watching de Beauchamp's cheeks getting redder and redder.

'They want an afternoon off?' repeated de Beauchamp.' A whole afternoon?'

'Yes, my lord,' said Philbert.

'And what about my turnip crop?' asked de Beauchamp. 'Are they proposing to significantly increase that in return?'

'I'm afraid their position on the turnips remains steadfast.' his manservant said.

'And so why, pray tell me, why do they think I should give them an afternoon off?' the Baron continued.

'I, ah... I believe it's customary at around this time of the year for the servants to be given a half day's holiday, my lord,' said Philbert, adding, after a slight pause, 'it's considered good practice among the nobility.'

'Is it, Philbert? Is it?' De Beauchamp's tone suggested that the employer benefits were not immediately apparent to him. He took a deep lungful of air in an effort to remain calm. 'And just why do they want an afternoon off?'

'Tomorrow is Shrovetide, my lord. The peasants will be celebrating before the onset of Lent. And they have asked that their celebrations might be aided by a half day in order that they might eat, drink and make merry. It's traditional, my lord, for them to engage in sports and games.'

'Sports and games?' said his lord. 'What kind of sports and games?'

'Traditional English ones, my lord.' Philbert replied. 'I believe they involve balls.'

'Most of them do,' snorted de Beauchamp, 'can't you be any more specific?'

'Well, my lord, there is one particular game enjoyed by the

peasantry that involves two teams competing to see who is able to score the most points by kicking a ball past the opposing side's boundary line. When the playing time is finished, the team that has accumulated the most points is the winner.'

The Baron stared at his manservant. 'It sounds utterly facile.' he said. Édouard de Beauchamp was not known for his sporting prowess.

'It's a traditional game, my lord.' repeated his servant.

'Hmpphh,' said de Beauchamp, 'I might have known it would be a tradition.'

In addition to the unruly ways of the English, de Beauchamp also found their customs, and what they claimed as their culture, bizarre beyond reckoning. And now, it seemed, the English had dredged up another ludicrous so-called tradition that appeared to consist of nothing more complex than kicking a ball up and down a field for however long it took for the opposition to get tired. He was not at all surprised that it had been so easy to conquer the English. They were a primitive people, and deeply infuriating. Whatever the issue was, it seemed to him that anything the English wished to do which he wished them not to do, was always upheld as some inviolable tradition, the elimination of which was tantamount to sacrilege. And whenever he took steps to implement his land-lordly rights, peasant labour was swiftly withdrawn until such time as the Baron realised the apparent error of his ways. This time, however, he was determined to exercise his authority. De Beauchamp drew himself up to his full height, which was not great, and gave his response.

'The answer, Philbert, is no. I'll say it again – no. This estate is losing revenue quicker than a cracked barrel loses wine, and it's all down to that rabble out there. If they won't work then I'm not giving them half a day off to kick a ball about and eat pancakes. Absolutely not.' He waited for a reply. 'Well?'

'Ah… very good, sir, very good.' Philbert de Vexin rounded his lips as if to continue but then thought better of it. De Beauchamp glanced around.

'Is that it, Philbert? Or is there something else?'

His manservant did his uncomfortable shuffle once more.

'Just one small thing, my lord.'

'Well, come on then. Let's be having it.'

Philbert reached into the pocket of his tunic and pulled out an impressive looking piece of parchment, sealed with a large blob of dirty red wax and embossed with an unmistakeable stamp. He handed it to de Beauchamp, whose face visibly drained of colour as he recognised the seal.

As he took the parchment, his mouth flapped open repeatedly but no intelligent sound was forthcoming.

'It's the King, my lord.' said Philbert de Vexin.

'It's the King, Philbert!' The Baron finally managed to get the words out. 'What does he want?'

'I'm sorry, my lord, I have not taken the liberty of opening the letter to find out.' Philbert said.

'Yes, yes,' said de Beauchamp, fumbling with the seal. He unfolded the letter and the last remnant of colour vanished from his cheeks. He slumped down into his chair and stared vacantly at his servant.

'Is everything alright, my lord?'

'Is everything alright? Are you mad, Philbert? It's the King! He is sending men to collect the debt we owe!'

Philbert had feared as much when he saw the letter. Although both he and de Beauchamp had known for sometime that the estate was underproducing, they had both felt that perhaps there was still time to turn things around. It appeared, however, that this was not the case, and what was bad for his lord would inevitably be bad for Philbert de Vexin too. The plural pronoun had not gone unnoticed by de Beauchamp's manservant.

'What are we going to do, Philbert?'

'We, my lord?'

'Precisely, WE.' continued Baron Édouard de Beauchamp. Panic had set in and his large round head was becoming even redder than usual. 'We haven't got the cash and we've got no way of accumulating it before they get here! And instead of doing what they're supposed to do, the peasants are on the verge of revolt because I won't let them slack off work to play some ridiculous ball game!'

'When exactly will the King's men arrive, my lord?' Philbert asked.

De Beauchamp ran his eyes over the letter again and almost fainted when he found the information. 'Oh dear God! They should be here tomorrow! What am I going to do?'

At this point the servant felt that he too needed to sit down. Normally he would not have done so in front of his master but on this occasion he judged that the impending crisis justified abnormal reactions. The Baron, in fact, took this to be a positive sign. The man's servile qualities left much to be desired but he was a lateral thinker, and de Beauchamp was hoping against hope that he might just be able to come up with some way out of the mire that de Beauchamp now found himself in.

Philbert looked pointedly and said, 'My lord, I have it.'

De Beauchamp jumped out of his seat and grasped his manservant by the hand. Anxiety was spread across the whole of his face.

'What? What is it? The plague or a plan? What have you got?' he demanded.

His crafty servant smiled a slow smile. 'I have a solution to the problem, my lord,' he said. 'I shall need a pig, a sack of pulses and a small amount of ready cash. Give me these,' he said, 'and I promise you that when the King's men arrive tomorrow they will find no reason to harass you.'

In front of Beauchamp and de Vexin was a horde of around two hundred and fifty dirty-faced peasants, screaming like deranged savages and waving their fists at anyone foolish enough to come within spitting distance of them. What made the crowd doubly fearsome was the fact that around half of them had stripped to the waist, including not a few women, and were beating their chests in a terrifying display. Philbert, despite his earlier bravado, was visibly cowering in the face of the onslaught, and any confidence that de Beauchamp had had in his manservant evaporated instantly. The

Baron felt his bowels loosen as he contemplated the total and utter disaster before him. Not only were the King's men destined to find no annual cash payment forthcoming, but when they arrived they would find a raging, violent revolt in full swing and he seemingly powerless in the face of it. It appeared that the crowd were not at all happy at his less than full support of their sporting intentions.

As the fear and the fury rose inside him he found that he could not tear his eyes from the riotous scene unfolding on the village green. Finally, when he could stand no more the war cries and profanities being flung at him by the angry crowd, he swung round to vent his fury at de Vexin. But it was too late. The King's men had arrived. Instead of his scrawny manservant, he found himself looking at the shining silver breast-plate of a mounted knight. But instead of the brutish giant de Beauchamp had expected, this knight had eyes that were wide with barely suppressed fear at least on a par with his own.

'What in the name of Our Lord is happening here?!' croaked the knight.

Swallowing hard and trying greatly to remain calm, he cleared his throat and with the greatest of efforts attempted a casual greeting. 'Oh, good morning, Sir Knight. Allow me to introduce myself – my name is Édouard de Beauchamp, welcome to my manor. Ah, this is Philbert de Vexin my manservant. As you can see.'

'Shut up!' bellowed the knight. 'Have you entirely lost your senses? Look!'

De Beauchamp looked. In front of him the baying mob had

picked up one of their number and flung him high into the air. As he watched the airborne youth, he saw that in his hands he held the severed head of another man which, at the height of his rise into the air, he threw high into the sky. As the boy fell to the ground with a sickening crunch there was a fearful cheer from the crowd who fell upon the head like pack animals upon a piece of meat.

'What in God's name is it!?' bawled the knight, his voice trembling.

The party of twenty five men behind him shrank back further from the crowd. At this point Philbert threw himself to his knees in front of the knight.

'Oh, Sir Knight!' he exclaimed, 'Sir Knight, how glad we are that you have come to save us from this wretched mob!'

The Baron slapped his hand to his sweating forehead and felt that at any moment his already loose bowels would give way.

'Sir Knight,' wailed Philbert, with an enthusiasm born of extreme desperation, 'you are our only hope! For a week we have cowered before this baying mob who desire our blood. They refuse all our attempts at reason and they refuse to work their land!'

At this, de Beauchamp's mouth fell open. What in God's name was his servant doing? Before him, the mob had begun chasing the severed and bloody head across the village green. It was a cruel and vicious chase and no mercy was shown to any who fell in their way. One ill-fated soul who had reached out to exact his own revenge on the head was brutally pulled aside and stabbed in the neck. He watched in horror as another had his arm wrenched from the socket. In another corner of the field a select group had given up entirely on chasing the head and had set to work erecting a makeshift gallows, for which they already had a waiting queue of unfortunates. It was a fearsome sight, made all the more disquieting by the sudden and frightening roar that erupted from the crowd as one of them succeeded in kicking the head past the weed-filled duck pond at the far end of the village green. Immediately, a large number of the bare-chested peasants fell upon each other, pummelling their apparent compatriots with alarming brutality.

'God in heaven!' the knight exclaimed. 'What are they doing? They have fallen into civil infraction! Anarchy is all around us! Society is breaking down!'

The crowd, apparently hearing the knight's cries, momentarily ceased their infighting as one of their number threw into the air what looked like a second decapitated head.

The knight wailed, 'They've killed another one! They're vitriolic! They delight in mutilating their victims!'

As the newly severed head hit the ground, Philbert de Vexin almost choked in horror. 'I recognise the head!' he cried. 'My lord! It is that of Sir Roger de Carradice!'

Sir Roger de Carradice was one of Édouard de Beauchamp's most loyal knights. Faint with the realisation that the mob were not about to spare anyone, he feared that he, their lord and master, might very well be next on the list. This realisation was made all the more probable by the sudden about turn of the crowd who had now begun stampeding towards the very area where the Baron, Philbert, the large knight and his men were cowering.

'What on earth did you do to provoke this mob?!' screamed the knight.

'Nothing, nothing at all,' de Beauchamp shouted, struggling to find rhyme or reason to explain the riot unfolding before him.

'Well,' he added, 'I wouldn't give them half a day off to kick a ball about, and they didn't like that very much.'

By now the angry mob were gaining ground fast. The knight fixed him with a wide-eyed stare and spoke quickly, the fear making it difficult for him to get his words out.

'Baron de Beauchamp, I have twenty five men with me. We cannot possibly take on this rampaging horde. It is quite obvious to me that you are the victim of an attempted usurpation and under such circumstances it would be impossible for us to return with you to the manor to collect your annual payment. If you will take my advice, you will return to the Manor House and lay store for a siege. I and my men shall return with reinforcements.'

'When?' asked de Beauchamp, suddenly panicking at the thought of being abandoned to the pack of baying animals fast approaching. 'When will you return with reinforcements?'

'Difficult to say.' stammered the knight. 'Very soon, of course.'

By now the crowd were just a stone's throw away. De Beauchamp looked on helplessly as one of the mob picked up the bloodied head from the ground, where it was being kicked along by the pack. Still running, the man threw the head high above him and as it descended to earth he kicked it with such force as the Baron had never before witnessed. Instantly, the head split open, spilling brains and blood as it arced high into the air on a clear trajectory towards where he stood rooted to the spot in fear. The knight and his men, their eyes like saucers, stared in horror at the spectacle, before the knight, suddenly shaken from his torpor, stretched his mouth wide and shouted the command that no true knight of the King should ever shout: 'RETREAT!'

Instantly, the knight's men turned on their heels and ran. De Beauchamp, his arms flailing wildly, turned to Philbert and screamed for as long as the air in his lungs would allow it: 'RUN!'

They ran, but the severed head flying through the air towards them was quicker, and as de Beauchamp stumbled up the hill he heard an almighty whooshing sound and the head slammed into the back of him, knocking him to the ground and covering him entirely with mud, blood and spilt brains. The noble Baron did not have a strong constitution and so it was perhaps fortunate that at that point he fainted.

'Are you alright, my lord?'

He opened his eyes to see his manservant fanning him with the parchment letter that had announced the impending arrival of the knight and his men. He looked around him and realised that he was sitting in his chair in the Great Hall of the Manor House. There was no baying mob and no severed head to be seen.

De Beauchamp rubbed his eyes and then looked at Philbert. 'What happened?' he asked.

'You were hit on the back of the head, my lord. However, fear not. The problem is solved.'

Édouard de Beauchamp sat up. 'The problem is solved?!' he said, agog. 'How in the name of all God's creatures can you stand there and tell me the problem is solved!? I have been the victim of a rampaging mob, the King's men have departed, leaving us to fend for ourselves, and the King himself, when he gets wind of the disaster, will in all probability strip me of my land and titles and cast me into the darkest dungeon currently available! How on earth can you say that the problem is solved?!'

De Beauchamp slumped back, overcome by the miserableness of the situation.

'If you will permit me, my lord, I can explain everything.' said Philbert.

De Beauchamp simply stared at him.

'There is no problem, my lord, because there is no baying mob.'

Again, he looked at him, confused.

'To be more precise,' Philbert continued, 'the baying mob that you witnessed were in no way directing their violence towards you.'

'Who on earth were they directing their violence towards then?' asked the Baron.

'Not who, my lord, but what. The scene you witnessed on the village green was not a riot at all, but a simple ball game.'

The words took a little time to sink in.

'A ball game?' repeated de Beauchamp, incredulous.

'Yes, my lord. A ball game. A particularly violent one, but, nonetheless, a ball game.'

'But…What…? How…?' stammered de Beauchamp.

His servant smiled smugly.

'It was really very simple, my lord.' he began. 'Clearly, we needed some way of stopping the King's knights from finding out that we don't yet have the money we owe. What better way of doing that than staging a mock riot thus preventing them from entering onto manor land?'

'A mock riot? Mock? But the mob...? I don't understand.'

'Ah,' said Philbert, 'the mob. You will remember that they had asked you for a half day's holiday, to celebrate before the onset of Lent?'

'Yes...' said de Beauchamp cautiously.

'Well, my lord, I knew that the sports and games they had planned were highly likely to be extremely violent affairs, so violent in fact as to look to any outside observer exactly like a riot. So I simply paid them a visit last night in their local hostelry and gave them a whole day off. Plus several flagons of cider, paid for with your generous cash advance, to incite them a little further.'

The Baron de Beauchamp was still confused. 'But what about the severed head, and the unfettered violence, and the blood and the brains?' he asked.

'Ah yes, the severed head that the crowd appeared to be kicking was in fact a pig's bladder stuffed with beans, hence my request for the pig and the pulses. The blood that it was covered in was a mixture of the pig's and the crowd's, and the beans, once they were covered in blood and mud, looked uncannily like brains. Beans, brains, blood, mud – all a sham. The violence, on the other hand, was entirely genuine.'

Édouard de Beauchamp was not convinced. 'But what about the head of Roger de Carradice? I saw it with my own eyes!'

'If I might correct you, my lord, you did not see it very clearly.

You believed it was the head of Roger de Carradice simply because I told you that it was.'

Slowly the realisation dawned.

'Philbert,' he cried, 'you're a genius! The players looked like a vicious angry mob, and the King's men were so terrified by the sight of them that they took flight immediately without even bothering to stay and collect the cash!'

'Precisely, my lord,' said Philbert.

'What a game!' exclaimed de Beauchamp? 'So fearsome and violent that the royal army chooses to flee rather than face its players!' He paused. 'Not sure I like the look of that as a sport for gentlemen though,' he added.

Philbert nodded. 'They call it gameball, my lord. I believe that game is their old English word for battle.'

The Baron shuddered. 'Typically English,' he said, 'violent, unrestrained and uncontrollable. What are the rules?'

'There aren't any. I believe the aim of the game is to kick the bladder through the goals of the opposing team as many times as possible. The score was forty two nil when we left.'

'Forty two nil? Good grief - how long does the game last?'

'Usually around four days to a week,' replied Philbert de Vexin, 'it varies.'

'Well how do you know when it's ended?' asked de Beauchamp, confused.

'Generally it ends when the majority of players are either dead or fatally injured,' answered Philbert, 'it depends really on how many players are on each team.'

'And how many is that, usually?'

'Generally speaking, around two hundred. It's not a game for the faint-hearted.'

'No.' mused Édouard de Beauchamp. He rubbed his beard. 'Grateful as I am, Philbert, I can't see it catching on, you know. Far too violent.'

'Very unlikely, my lord,' said his manservant, 'a fringe pursuit, at best.'

The Baron suddenly slumped down into his chair again.

'Is anything the matter, my lord?' Philbert asked, concerned.

De Beauchamp sighed heavily. 'It was undeniably a brilliant plan, but you realise of course that this doesn't solve the problem of the money. We're still short of what we need because the peasants won't do what we ask them.'

His vassal smiled again. 'On the contrary, my lord. The peasants were so happy that you gave them a full day off, rather than just a half day, that they have promised to return to work with a renewed vigour. By the time Sir Knight and the King's men return I am fully confident that we will have the requisite sum ready for collection.'

'That's no use, Philbert!' cried de Beauchamp. 'We need the money now, not by next year's harvest!'

'If you'll permit me, my lord, I had not entirely finished. You are, of course, wholly right that the revenue the peasants will produce will come far too late to be of any use to us this year. Consequently, I took the liberty of using the money I asked you for to put down a small wager on the outcome of the game before the King's men arrived.'

'A wager?' he asked, feeling the sweat dripping from his brow once more. 'How much of a wager?'

'I will not trouble you with the indignities of monetary matters, my lord, save to say that my speculation was proved correct. You now, sire, have more than enough to pay off the King.'

Édouard de Beauchamp was momentarily caught between elation and the realisation that his servant had almost gambled away a significant amount of his personal fortune. He made a strained sound.

'That's all very well, but what if they'd lost?!' he asked, his voice barely above a squeak.

'Unlikely, my lord. I used the money that was left over from the wager to bribe the opposing side to lose.'

The relief for de Beauchamp was instantaneous.

'Brilliant, Philbert!' he cried. 'I couldn't have organised it better myself!'

'No, my lord…' said Philbert.

'So,' continued de Beauchamp, 'in view of the morning's excitement, and in recompense for your loyal service, I am giving you a half day's holiday, effective immediately.'

'Why thank you, my lord,' his servant said. 'I am almost overcome with gratitude.'

'Think nothing of it, Philbert.' said Baron de Beauchamp magnanimously. 'We must endeavour to rule by praise and reward rather than by fear.'

'Quite right, my lord.'

Édouard de Beauchamp looked out of the diamond-paned

window in front of him and surveyed the fields that stretched out into the distance. The noon-day sun shone brightly down, lighting up the rows of unploughed furrow that would soon be filled with the leafy heads of purple and white turnips. Undoubtedly, the English were hooligans. And their sporting endeavours were questionable in the extreme. But he was forced to admit that their simple game of "football", or whatever they called it, had saved his neck, and for this he was willing to revise his opinion of them. Compromise, he thought, was the fulcrum of diplomacy, and he quietly congratulated himself on his expert ability to extract the best from a situation – even if this was a violent, unrestrained and uncontrollable gameball match.

Football, wherein is nothing but beastly fury, and extreme violence, whereof proceedeth great hurt, and consequently rancour and malice do remain with them that be wounded.

Thomas Eyot, 1499-1546:
Book Of The Governor (1531)

Viking trek

by Arne Hanssen

The early action takes place in Norway, land of fjords and forests. Though it is actually the recent past, the setting is a timeless one. The opening view, from high up, is a panorama of treetops, conifers spreading far away into the Nordic distance. Like the opening shots to The Sound of Music the view zooms in on a clearing where two powerful men are at work sawing rhythmically at a tree…

At either end of the double-handed saw stands a tall blond-haired man. As one pulls the blade, the other pushes. As one pushes, the other pulls. That way, the tree will soon be felled. The men are called Anders and Bjorn. Anders is big and strong. He loves Hilde and he loves Leeds United. Bjorn is also big and strong. He loves Hedwig and he too loves Leeds United.

The woods around Tromso echo to their labours and, as the sawing goes to and fro, so does their conversation:-

'Johnny Giles was the greatest midfielder.'

'Says who, Anders?'

'Says my father.'

'He is a fine man.'

'He is.'

'Billy Bremner was actually the greatest.'

'Says who, Bjorn?'

'Says my father.'

'He is a fine man.'

'And so he is.'

'Perhaps they were both the greatest?' Anders offers as a compromise.

'I think so,' Bjorn agrees, 'because they are great friends. And then we had Nick Barmby.'

'He is only equal to Bremner and Giles in height.'

Anders and Bjorn laugh heartily since, although sadly true, it is still a good joke by Norwegian standards.

Anders J Olafsson and Bjorn B Johansson, two of Norway's finest, have been Leeds supporters ever since either of them can remember. Children of the first generation of Scandinavian Leeds fans in the '70s, they have stuck with the club through thick and thin, with a devotion bordering on the manic, saving up to repeat the Viking trek to Elland Road three times a year. They can remember Leeds winning the Championship. They can remember, with pain, just how recently they have been in the Champions League semi-final.

But, even more recently, they have been doing little other than trying to forget disappointment after disappointment. On this particular morning, they feel nervy. Yesterday, another embarrassing defeat for the not-so-super-Whites had been paraded across frozen lands, beaming into timber framed dwellings shivering in the Arctic winter. As they near the paper mill that employs them, their edginess grows.

'They are bound to be here somewhere.' Anders mutters as they walk through the gates and almost as soon as he has said it, Lars and Nils, lying in wait in their Vodaphone shirts behind the pulp pile, spring out to mock them.

'Yoo-hoo troloo!' Lars pronounces, triumphal.

'Yoo-hoo troloo!' echoes Nils in equal triumph.

'Another defeat for your team.' Lars says, knowing exactly how to state the obvious to his workmates in the most annoying way possible. It turns out to be a couple of mocking yoo-hoo troloos too many. Big strong men can take only so much ribbing and the two Man United fans will pay the price for their goading. Today, there will be a curious pinkish tinge to Batch 32 at Linskopping Paper Mill. In a furious couple of moments, Lars and Nils are both deprived of their footie shirts forever, and of the ability to walk straight for several weeks. The works manager tries in vain to obtain statements from anyone, including the badly bruised couple. Their silence is in every way connected to the fear of even worse treatment next time. The duty foreman, though, does happen to overhear Bjorn saying something to Anders about enough being enough and that the sons-of-wolfbitches had it coming to them.

Even for boys as obstinately dedicated to Leeds as these two, such an event has to prove a turning point and so it is. The two die-hard Leeds fans are forced to bravely face the truth. It can't go on like this. They agree they must decide whether or not to continue supporting a great but struggling club on the other side of the North Sea. The Paper Mill is growing tired of the halt to tree-felling every time a Leeds story breaks and their best loggers hurry off to tune in to Sky Sports on the canteen's TV. Insultingly, the management have in desperation threatened to replace them with a single chainsaw. Girlfriends have, coincidentally, delivered ultimatums; football is ruling everyone's lives. Anders' mum has even suggested him redecorating his room, saying the Leeds United wallpaper is fading and he could get new paper at a discount from work. They have to make a courageous decision and they do.

'Anders Johnny Olafsson, I think it is time to either quit following Leeds or quit our homes, our jobs and even our girlfriends.'

A painful truth has finally been faced. Following a far-off faded football force is insane. And they both know it.

'You are right, Bjorn Billy Johansson,' Anders replies with a twinkle in his eye, 'I think, perhaps, the girls in Leeds will be more understanding.'

The very next day, they pack in their jobs, say quick goodbyes to each bewildered girlfriend, gather up their belongings, including Ander's prized possession of a Viking doll (male!) in a Leeds kit and set off for England. In next to no time, the printing works of the Yorkshire Evening Post, Wellington Street, Leeds, gains the services of two powerful new employees in the bulk paper section. They are prepared to work hard and they are also prepared, if they find any Vodaphone vipers in their midst, to mete out the same paper-pinking punishment.

Viking Invasion

Now the action moves entirely to England. Several months pass. The printing works of the Yorkshire Evening Post in Leeds has begun to grow accustomed to the oddly musical strains of spoken and shouted Norwegian rising above the hum of the presses.

It has been generally agreed at the works that nobody can remember seeing anyone with the capacity to graft which matches the efforts of either Anders J Olafsson or Bjorn B Johansson. It is also agreed they are both "chuffing big lads".

"I wouldn't like to cross either of them" is an almost daily mantra and, if there is anyone at the printing works who doesn't support the local club, they are keeping pretty quiet about it. Bjorn and Anders are well liked, keep the canteen in healthy profit and can even speak a few words of English by now. And, whenever they sing, they always do so in English even if their choice is rather limited. They have a repertoire of three songs; Glory Glory Leeds United, Leeds United Calypso and Marching on Together.

"Now little Billy Bremner is the captain of the crew" is quite probably Bjorn B's favourite lyric of all time, giving Glory, Glory an extra jollity. He's not sure, though, because he really loves the third line too - "His hair is red and fuzzy and his body black and blue" - *Fuzzy* being the word he dwells on longest in tribute to the loving way it was sung on the original Ronnie Hilton recording.

They don't quarrel much but Anders, for patriotic reasons, is always thrilled to sing, "Proud and tall in the goalmouth stands the Viking" in tribute to Gary Sprake who starred for Don Revie's

Leeds legends.

'It is a mighty line, Anders.' Bjorn informs him.

'Indeed it is, Bjorn Johansson.'

Once in a while, they don't talk about football for minutes at a stretch. This is largely because they both now have English girlfriends. The Old Peacock on Elland Road has long been famed as, if not the spiritual home of Scandinavian Leeds fans, at least the closest watering hole to that spiritual home. And, on top of it being their favourite place of relaxation, it is the pub which has now provided the Norwegian newcomers with a welcome love interest.

Michelle and Eileen had just popped in to have a drink, having spent £120 between them on merchandise in the club shop. Clutching their LUFC bags close to their hearts, they happened to be sitting at a table next to Anders and Bjorn and were incredibly touched by the site of two grown, in fact overgrown, men, sitting dewy-eyed, staring out of the pub window at the football ground opposite. It must remain a mystery how Michelle could find Anders "cute" at 6 feet 2 in height. It must remain an even greater mystery how Eileen could find Bjorn cute" at 6 feet 4. It is less of a mystery how they could be touched by such a scene. The boys had virtually no English at their disposal, the girls were entirely bereft of Norwegian but the language of football love is universal. Waggling their shopping bags at them, the girls moved in.

'Hiiiii, I'm Eileen and this is Michelle. You don't happen to be Leeds fans by any chance, do you?'

Bjorn spoke for them both. Although he said something like,

'Jeg er lei meg hva did du si?' He meant, 'I'm sorry, what did you say?'

'Oooooo,' Michelle quivered, 'that sounds gorgeous.'

Turning to Anders, she said, 'And what is your name big boy?'

A flummoxed but enraptured Anders could only say, 'Meg Engelske er meget fattig.' which means, of course, 'My English is very poor.'

'Oooooo, a double-barrelled name.' Michelle cooed to a delighted Eileen.

After this, love was bound to ensue – and it quickly did.

'Jeg elske du/I love you.' flutters regularly to and fro because Anders now loves Leeds United and he loves Michelle. Bjorn loves Leeds United and he loves Eileen.

It is remarkable how quickly someone can learn English when there is enough incentive. Mere weeks it takes for the boys and girls to be chattering away about all things Leeds. Soon, too, Anders trusts Michelle enough to show her his Viking doll (male!) without embarrassment. And just as soon, plans are afoot to get more involved in the local supporters' club.

'Any ideas for a mascot?' Eileen asks.

'I've just had an idea.' muses Michelle.

Such momentous changes in the lives of the two friends are bound to inspire deep and serious discussion between them. And they do so - usually whilst drinking in The Old Peacock.

'Anders, I have found great happiness since moving to Leeds.'

Bjorn admits.

'The same is true for me.' The reply comes readily. 'but,' Anders continues, 'there is one thing that does sadden me, Bjorn.'

'What is that?'

'That Leeds were bad before and are complete rubbish now.'

'Sadly, that is true.' Bjorn concedes. 'Perhaps it is too much to have everything in this life.' he continues, surprising himself by his deep thinking.

He certainly surprises Anders who takes several moments to absorb this before replying.

'Surely we must stay in Leeds, even if it is many years before United are mighty again.'

'Surely. We owe it to Michelle and to Eileen.' Bjorn says as he stands up and takes a devoted look at the stadium.

The scene closes with him turning, empty beer glasses in hand, headed for the bar.

Plunder, pillage...

It is a foggy cold and damp December during the first English winter for our two Scandinavian giants. It is the Christmas Party for the Headingley Branch of the Leeds United Supporters Club and the village hall is crowded with Leeds fans in fancy dress. There can be no denying the branch's great spirit is centred round the dynamic foursome of Anders, Michelle, Bjorn and Eileen whose enthusiasm has invigorated the local support in a few short months. In a recent

Branch survey of video favourites, The *Heroes of Telemark* and *The Vikings* ran *Wembley '72* a close race in terms of popularity.

Life has been good following their impulsive decision to flit to England. Being able to see their favourite team on a weekly basis, even if they are rubbish, is a source of such happiness that they couldn't care less about such poor weather. Since they are well-used to nad-freezing weather anyway, this doesn't even qualify as a proper winter for them, it's more like July. The concern they feel about having bare legs is purely because they are not all that happy to be dressed as the Norse gods Woden and Thor.

'Anders J Olafsson, do you feel a mighty fool dressed as Woden, even if we please both girls?'

'Truly, Bjorn B Johansson,' Anders replies by way of confirmation, 'I feel more foolish than a falling lemming.'

"Thor" can only nod in agreement.

Festive trimmings bedeck the hall, even if there is much more blue, white and yellow on show than evergreen. Coca Cola red is totally absent and "Santa" is some guy in his mid-twenties in a Leeds United tracksuit and a fake white beard. Propped against a wall is the new supporters' club mascot, a seven foot cardboard cut-out Viking, whose painted on, blond and fuzzy locks are meant to hint at both Billy Bremner and Gary Sprake. Its shield has been smartly painted up in Leeds colours by Eileen. Now his steely glare casts out in the direction of all opposing fans. In a matter of weeks, its presence at both home and away games has become a thing of legend. And of envy.

The room hums with boozy joy. Woden and Thor are enjoying the earthly pleasures of good Yorkshire ale whilst the girlie goddesses imbibe clear spirits known to humans as gin and tonics. There is nothing like belonging and feeling a part of something big. Everywhere the gods look, they see nothing but Leeds fans, some dressed as caterpillars, some as film stars, with the obligatory batch of nuns, but Leeds fans all. Suddenly, though, the merriment is punctured with a discovery.

'Quick, quick! They've nicked our Viking!' comes a shout.

Panic. Confusion. Possible plunder. Potential pillage. Whatever next? People run in all directions. In all the chaos, someone else shouts, 'It's the Devonshire Branch. They've grabbed the mascot. After them!'

A handful of the Devonshire Branch are there all right and making for the front door, but somehow the huge mascot has disappeared in all the confusion. Pointless though it may seem, each of the infiltrators is searched in case they have hidden a seven foot cardboard cut out down their trousers.

Outside, a car engine is running frantically on the spot. It is the getaway car waiting to complete the heist and at the wheel is the wife of the mascotnapper-in-chief playing Bonnie to his Clyde, her heart racing at the same speed as the car. Her eyes are fixed on the emergency exit. Any second she hopes to see the plunder brandished, then they're away.

There are two doors between the main room of the village hall and freedom. They are linked by a long corridor along which

"Clyde" is struggling. The Viking mascot is gripped firmly in both hands, but, it being taller than him by almost two feet, progress is painfully slow as he manoeuvres it past photocopiers, boxes of crisps and stacked cartons of Christmas decorations.

As Bonnie knows, Clyde is in reality Chairman of the Devonshire Whites. The "brilliant idea" to abduct the Headingley Whites' mascot and demand a ransom is all his own. In the confusion, no one has followed him from the room yet. It will all be worth it if he can just get the blasted thing out without decapitating it along the way.

Finally he reaches the door, manages to prop the Viking against the wall like a giant drunk, reaches for the handle and pulls. As he prepares to flee, he has the sense of a sudden, near-total eclipse. Woden is standing full-square in the doorway, barring all hope of passing. The terrified pillager negotiates a sudden turn, pirouetting in tandem with his trophy with the agility of a tango dancer and plunges back down the corridor. His efforts are soon seen to be futile though, as he looks up and sees his last hope barred, this time by Thor. The gods appear full of fury and so now the game is up.

'Dear, dear, little man,' says Thor, 'you are trapped.'

'A fine word, trapped.' Woden returns. 'He truly is trapped, like a reindeer in a ravine.'

'He must be punished.' Thor declares with a godlike finality.

'This is so,' Woden adds, 'but I have seen this man at Elland Road. Since you are a Leeds fan, your punishment will be only light, this time, little man.' The captured, cowed pillager submits meekly to the wrath of the gods.

Minutes later, the would-be Viking thief finally arrives at the overheating getaway car. His wife is in a lather. He is not. Having been lifted upside down by Woden and dangled over the toilet bowl while Thor, the thunder god, repeatedly turned the handle, he brokenly climbs into the passenger seat, flushed with failure.

The closing scene of this episode is of the heroes returning to the hall brandishing the saved mascot. General cheers and applause engulf them. Successive close-ups would show Eileen looking in admiration at Bjorn Billy Johansson, Michelle looking with love on Anders Johnny Olafsson. Steadily the happy view recedes until the village hall doors close, barring further sight of the festivities. A pan through ninety degrees captures the sight of a departing car, heading presumably for Devon.

This should be the cue for the evening to close on an absolute high and it is trying to for the four lovebirds but the advent of the mobile phone is forcing storytelling to play catch up and, even at a time of unalloyed joy, misery intervenes. A text message reaches Bjorn.

He looks up from its screen towards three worried faces and for two of them he translates, 'Mama's ill. I must go home.'

The last part of the saga requires a split screen to display simultaneous action. The day is cool and cloudy, reflecting inner mood. Initially blurred, the background gradually becomes clearer to reveal:

A close-up of Anders' face shows he has not been crying. It is not something he would do but he is clearly distraught. A head and shoulders shot widens out to reveal that he is sitting at the Billy Bremner statue at Elland Road. Thoughts run through his head; memories of the trek he and Bjorn made and of the sacrifice his friend has made. It will not be the same, for all the consolation of having his girlfriend Michelle and living near his team. He looks forlornly at the statue of his friend's hero until, at length, he shrugs, stands up and makes his way across to The Old Peacock, seeking consolation.

A close up of Bjorn in a forest glade. The huge double saw stands rusting and unused, propped against a tree. A chainsaw rests alongside a mountainous woodpile. It will not be the same. He has his home, his family, including a thankfully recovered mama but he wonders if maybe he has sacrificed too much. Zoom in to a parting shot of a face suddenly fixed with resolution but whether it signals good news for Anders, Eileen and Michelle, good news for Linskopping Paper Mill's productivity levels, or terrible news for the Vodaphone boys, Lars and Nils, is far from certain.

Wembley 73

by Neil Jeffries

> "I'll never play at Wembley again, unless I play at
> Wembley again."
>
> Kevin Keegan

One man's meat is another man's poison, said somebody, once upon a time. No idea who, but he or she was spot on come a sunny day in Lowestoft, April 1973. There was I walking to school, aged 13, with hardly a care in the world save for the fact that Slade's Cum On Feel The Noize had just dropped out of the chart and my haircut made me look a bit like a girl rather than their oh-so-cool bass player Jim Lea. I was two hundred miles from Elland Road but my personalised pencil case and school exercise book covers took me much closer. I could name thirty-three Leeds players and many of them had never even played for the first team. I took an insane delight in knowing I was perhaps the only person in Lowestoft who had heard of Nigel Davey, a full-back who had been at the club about 10 years and only played about a dozen games. I guess you could say I was mad about Leeds.

That sunny day I was already hot in my hated school blazer and felt an extra flush of embarrassment as I saw Mr Bishop the schoolteacher, who lived three doors up the street from me, walking across the playground towards me. Other kids in the school knew he was my neighbour and although he rarely taught me, even knowing a teacher was a sometimes uncomfortable privilege. Privilege, however, was about to go to a crazy new level.

'Are you doing anything on Saturday week?' he grinned, adding even before I could muster an answer, 'I've got two tickets spare for the Cup Final. Do you want them?'

My mind raced - elation, pride, confusion, doubt. Why would anyone not want to use the tickets? Are Leeds hated that much? Is he having me on? But no, his father was president of Lowestoft Town FC and had two spare tickets for the one hundred and first FA Cup Final between Leeds United and Sunderland

'Er, cor, yes please!'

I dare say my grin would've got me wedged in the classroom door. It can't have been long after that, though, that my mind raced to an inescapable conclusion: I could only go if my dad took me. Elation, pride, confusion evaporated but doubt remained. Would my dad, whose interest in football began and ended with kicking a ball in the park for five minutes to placate my sister and I, before crying off to buy us a *Zoom* and a *Funny Face*, even want to take me? In my heart I knew the answer: no. The offer of tickets was meat to me (in those days I still ate it) but a potential poison to dad. We got on well but we didn't share a taste for football at all. As a steel erector, he worked away during the week, living in digs. The weekends were his quality time, time with his family, relaxing. Professional football was something he'd take only a cursory interest in around a quarter to five on a Saturday because my mum would then be checking her Littlewood's Pools coupons. He wouldn't even want to watch it on the telly. I was mad to think he'd want to go. Getting him to take me, then, was a big deal. And yet, although I was certain he wouldn't want to be there, I knew he knew that for me this was a once in a lifetime opportunity so he'd smile, say yes and pretend he didn't mind. My dad was like that.

Wembley had no elevated walkway in those days, and certainly no giant steel arch. But the left one of the Twin Towers ahead of us looked like the ideal marker of where we would need to return to after the game. Dad made a few other mental notes and off we set. Him quite convinced he would remember where our coach was parked, me not so sure. But if I was good on Leeds, dad was good on details. I complemented him and joked about my being able to remember the names of the entire team. He smiled but I could tell he wasn't in the slightest bit interested. Even now. I had felt certain that he would become gripped by the atmosphere, that some of my enthusiasm would rub off on him. No sign of that. I might as well have been trying to get him to sit down and listen to my Slade singles. I kept telling myself not to look disappointed and to help him through the ordeal. And for him I could tell it was, if not exactly an ordeal, certainly an alien environment that was giving him cause for concern. With the coach location logged and committed to memory, he had two new concerns: one, losing me in the milling crowds; and two, hooligans. But as I handed over a handful of change in exchange for a white rosette with a tin-plate FA Cup in its centre there was another, far more serious threat neither of us had considered.

Checking our gate number on the tickets we turned right beneath the Twin Towers and headed towards our entrance. Within minutes, white silk scarves and blue-and-yellow trimmed rosettes vanished and red and black became the dominant colours. I felt physically sick. We checked the tickets again. It was a 50:50 chance that I'd never even considered but now it was obvious: we had lost and were condemned to spend the match at the wrong end of the ground. Crazy notions went through my head. Should we just turn round and go home? Should we go in and risk being beaten to a pulp? Had Mr Bishop known about this all along? Had that been what the grin on his face meant?

My father was nothing if not a pragmatist and calmly reasoned that if we were in the wrong place, then there might be a pair of Sunderland fans facing a similar predicament at the other end of the stadium. Hoping against hope we retraced out steps, back through the crush at the front of Wembley and round towards the Leeds turnstiles. As a Suffolk lad, all accents here were foreign to me but I somehow felt more at home as Wearside turned to Yorkshire, as red bar scarves turned to white. And yet I was still crushed, feeling utterly forlorn to be undertaking what I believed to be a fool's errand. This was crazy. We had been lucky once to even get here, I surely would not be so blessed as to get lucky again.

This idea didn't appear to have occurred to dad, though, as he led me through the crowds with a hopeful look spread across his face. Another logistical challenge to add to the day's roster of duties. As we reached the first of the stepped entrances, we looked for anyone wearing Sunderland colours. But all those we saw were heading purposefully in the opposite direction. My heart sank again.

I regret to admit that I wanted to cry. I recall a father's hand on my shoulder and an encouraging smile followed by the suggestion that we give it another ten minutes. That was easy, I'd rather stand here than go in with the opposition anyway. Then dad was talking to two of them, their red-and-white scarves as alien here as I'd felt a lifetime ago at the other end. Suddenly faces beamed and tickets were exchanged. For the first time today dad looked genuinely pleased to be here. Perhaps his face was reflecting the joy in my own, but my spirits soared and my dad was as big a hero as Allan Clarke.

Meeting that pair of similarly stranded Mackems was, of course, the last thing that would go right that day.

As our saviours hurried off waving back, we hurried forward into the maw of one of Wembley's giant entrances, the darkness inside as unforgettable as the contrasting shafts of light beaming down from the entrances above the steps into the actual stadium. The impact was instant. I was immediately enraptured by the atmosphere, enchanted by levels of emotion and anticipation all around. And yet I also felt alienated by the chanting, beery gangs shouting in accents that to me seemed as menacing as those we would have heard in the Sunderland end. Dad looked unimpressed and even more concerned. As the throng pushed and shoved he repeated his insistence that we stick together and go in and find a place to stand. No sense coming this far together only to get separated.

I'd been to Wembley before, for a couple of schoolboy and one full international, and I'd watched the last three Cup Finals on telly, but nothing had prepared me for the rush of that first step on to the terraces that day. The ground was a cauldron and Leeds fans were boiling over. The cockiness of supporting the best team radiated from every step around us. We pushed our way through, in search of a likely vantage point. As we did so I realised what was about to unfold and what unlikely odds we had both overcome to be right here, right now. And yet dad was still looking bemused. Like he felt he had been mad to agree to this. Then he took his first step into the mad world that I was inhabiting. After looking nervously around he grinned and observed that the Leeds fans were the noisiest. I welled with pride both at his confirmation of what I hoped was true, and that the buzz was starting to get to him, too. With around 20 minutes to kick-off my dad looked like he might actually enjoy himself. Finally, he seemed to have realised that we weren't about to be torn limb from limb by some knuckle-dragging bovver-booted skinhead, and had begun to relax. We had found a spot behind a crush barrier, quite close to an exit and could even see over the heads of the men in front. We gazed around, spotted official England mascot Ken Bailey in his red frock coat... and a banner reading "Norman Bites Yer Legs" away to our left. We joked about whether mum and sister, at home watching on BBC, would spot us. And we puzzled over another banner that appeared to be celebrating liquorice sweets, blissfully unaware that Pontefract was also a town in Yorkshire. As mad as the notion had once seemed, all the signs now suggested we were both glad to be here.

Majorettes gave way to the marching band of the Coldstream Guards and a rickety white staircase being wheeled out for Frankie

Vaughan to stand atop and lead the singing of Abide With Me. My dad liked Frankie Vaughan, might even have paid to see him once. The weather was far from my mind but it must have been dull because I'll never forget that when Frankie sang and waved his white boater the sun picked that very moment to shine. So what could possibly go wrong? Once the game kicked off it was clear that the answer was... most things.

The half-time whistle brought no respite, only the thought that barely forty-five minutes separated me and all around from humiliation and embarrassment. Dad could tell how I felt, and offered hopeful remarks, but I knew he couldn't feel the pain as I was. He'd done so much for me today, but he couldn't change the game, and I felt sorry that all his efforts looked like they were directed toward such a miserable dead end. But still he tried. Towards the end of the first half, presumably more in support of me than Leeds, I had noticed him joining in with some of the chants. Today this seems so unlikely but I know that he did. It was a remarkable effort. Now, as the marching band trooped off once more and the second half approached, I could tell that even he could sense my dread. He had become that rarest of creatures - a neutral wanting Leeds United to win.

The rest of the match passed for me in abject despair, wave after wave of broken attacks punctuated by ever more resigned glances at my wrist as the minute hand swept around towards a quarter to five. My dad sensing my misery and the general sense of hopelessness, suggested we leave early, to miss the crowds, but I asked one more favour of him. Leeds might score in the very last minute, or even injury time, and then there would be extra-time. And so we stayed. Me hoping against hope, he patiently waiting while I lived out every last second of my nightmare. At the whistle I remember clearly the sight of Sunderland manager Bob Stokoe doing a hop, skip and jump across the verdant turf. In the end dad, despite his desire to make a quick getaway, allowed me to hang around long enough to see the broken-hearted Leeds players collect their loser's medals. And then I could bear it no more and smiled a grim smile to dad that said yes, I was ready to go. And no, I didn't want to talk about it.

In retrospect this must have been the final poison of the day for my dad. The non-football fan who'd already given up a whole day to be surrounded by noisy then miserable Yorkshiremen. Having gone through all that, then for me to just clam up and sulk must have really put the mockers on the day. He deserved better. And yet he never complained.

I have absolutely no recollection of the journey home - except how easily we found the coach - but suspect that in the end my dad may even have enjoyed the day more than I had. Leeds United had let me down, for once, but my dad was there for me every step of the way. We both learned a lot that day, about how even the finest meat can sometimes be poisoned and even a poison can sometimes be palatable in the right company. We learned a lot about each other. And, however insane it seems, we enjoyed the experience much more than either of us had expected.

Leeds play like butchers.

Franz 'The Kaiser' Beckenbauer of Bayern
Munich at half time during the European Cup
Final, 1975.

Paris 75

by Ian Payne

> "They're the second best team in the world, and there's no higher praise than that."
>
> Kevin Keegan

I never got to see the second half of the European Cup Final in 1975 between my team, Leeds United and Bayern Munich - because I was sent to bed!

I was at a boarding school and, even though I was 13 years old, when the clock ticked round to 8.30 we had to troop off to the dormitory. It was the school rules. Bed time. This was the sort of thing they did at boarding school - when I was 18 I still wasn't allowed to go to a pub. We also had to wear school uniform whenever we went into Oxford so all the local tough kids could spot us from a mile away and spit at us. Pathetic really and it still makes my blood boil now, but that's boarding school for you.

We only had one television. It was black and white and had that odd, lightning fork, white line that moved diagonally across the screen all the time. As soon as one line disappeared another appeared at the top ad infinitum. Working nowadays in TV, I've learned it was called Ghosting and happened because we had a crap aerial. Then I just called it bloody annoying. Also, the TV was up on a shelf near the ceiling, which was annoying, too at a time when no one had remote controls.

I can remember every FA Cup Final from the 1970s, including, teams, scorers and times of goals. But ask me who played three years ago, or even last year and I'd have to think about it, and might not remember. Crumbling brains... so, many footballing memories from the 70s are strong but the memory of Paris 75 is by far the strongest and it still rankles.

I tried to watch the tiny screen as I backed away through the door and into the corridor along the horrible red-stained serrated linoleum.

The act of remembering that night brings thoughts of the wooden floorboards that gave you splinters if you didn't wear shoes, and even the tickly asbestos insulation they used round the water pipes in the TV room. It's as clear today as it was then and whenever I see grainy images of that game on television, I can feel the ire rising. There was nothing I could do about it. I was shaking, thumping the blankets of my bed and unable to sleep. I must have finally slept, goodness knows how.

Normally when you wake up, your mind flits around a bit, taking in the room - which bed am I in, have I slept enough, what's the time, what have I got on today? But this time there were none of those thoughts flitting around. I was straight into "What was the score?" mode. Because Leeds had come second so often I was expecting seriously bad news. You can try and push it away and use positive thinking techniques, but my mind went straight back to that match. I had to find out, which is when the frustration started all over again because......the radio just wouldn't tell me the bloody score. You know the feeling. Turn on the radio and the commentator doesn't tell you for ages. 'That's all we want to know!' I screamed then, and have a hundred times since.

I also remember suffering my first example of what I like to call the "News is always more important than sport syndrome" from which I was to suffer a lot at Radio 5-Live. The radio kept going on about hooliganism and people chucking seats in the stadium after the game, but no one would tell me the bleeding score. I can almost hear the news editor saying, 'Who cares about football when scenes like this can happen?' Well, er, I do...and I did. It was always the same when I worked for Radio 5-Live. The news people were always more interested in how many arrests there were at the match than the actual score. It's still going on. The opening line before 5-Live's coverage of the European Cup Final in Istanbul, May 2005 was, 'Good evening. Welcome to Turkey. Police say there's been no trouble here.' And the game itself...???!!!

Nothing's changed in 30 years.

Trying to find out if Leeds had won was so frustrating I felt like joining in with the fans and chucking my pillow onto the stadium pitch. Then the anger when the result finally came through. Leeds had LOST. Lost to cheating Germans and a cheating ref. Not-given penalties, disallowed goals, allowed goals, all that. Having watched the first half when we seemed so in control, I just couldn't believe it.

You can never watch repeats of games you've lost. Best to pretend they didn't happen. But many years later, I summoned the courage to watch the match including the 2nd half. I was even more amazed Leeds hadn't won. We were clearly the better side, and some of the decisions were...well...best not to go down that road. I was lucky enough to work with Jimmy Armfield, the Leeds manager in '75 and was fascinated to hear his take on the whole thing. Let's just say he has his doubts about the officials that night too. It's funny how those types of emotion can stay with you longer than so many other memories. Like when you smell something and it reminds you of an event years and years ago. A garden flower that you used to sniff when you were 5 years old.

Or sour grapes.

Hot Chilli Vodka at the Gristle Chop Café

by Peter Davies

> "Hungary is very similar to Bulgaria. I know they're
> different countries…"
>
> Kevin Keegan

I was in the Russian capital to watch Leeds United, my team and
my passion, play against Lokomotiv Moscow in the UEFA Cup. In
previous years, being drawn against a team from behind the former
Iron Curtain would have been reason for nerves. But in 1999, Leeds
were riding the crest of a wave, top of the Premiership and
progressing nicely in Europe. Protecting a 4-1 advantage from the
first leg at Elland Road, they were expected to coast through in
Moscow. These were good times for a team and fans long used to
disappointment. I travelled thousands of miles to see a football
match and, also, to have a glimpse at a crazy way of life.

Modern day Moscow is not what one might envision.
McDonald's outlets blight stylish inner-city concourses and there's
Cyrillic graffiti on the walls outside the Bolshoi. Gorky Park is a
third-rate theme park with rusted Ferris wheels and pony rides on
sagging steeds and not a trench-coated spy in sight. The metro
stations resemble museums, with artworks on the wall and
chandeliers tumbling from the ceilings. Moscow's nightlife is as
chaotic as nuclear fission with pricy, reckless diversions unheard of
just a decade or so ago. Hip young Muscovites boogie the night

away at hi-tech nightclubs which sprout like mushrooms after overnight rain. And, to judge from the reviews in *The eXile* weekly newspaper, have about the same lifespan. Gourmet restaurants flourish. Round-the-clock casinos prosper. Indeed, any preconceived notion of Moscow being home to taciturn locals shuffling about under gloomy skies is quickly exploded - like a puddle of slush under a Lada taxicab.

The Leeds United *team* is my passion. Unfortunately, the fans are not. Just as some parents should be made to pass a "fitness" test before having children, so I believe certain English soccer fans should be screened before being, as William Blake might have said, "loosed upon the world." Granted, ninety five per cent of my fellow Leeds United fans are happy to watch their side snatch yet another defeat from the jaws of victory, have a laugh and a beer and mope off home. But there's also a vicious mob of loons who scare the bejeezus out of most sane football followers. But once you travel away, that five per cent becomes more like fifty. Hordes of these hard core fans filled special flights from various English airports to join me and others on the Russian adventure.

I bumped into a couple of really iffy, white-scarved Yorkshiremen at various locales around Moscow. They weren't exactly intent on winning friends, but they were certainly trying to influence people. Particularly barmen, who they badgered for discount drinks at pubs like Armadillos, near Red Square. I also saw one meaty bloke with a Leeds crest tattooed on his forearm try and knock the black fur hat off an impassive soldier standing guard outside the Kremlin. The local "flathead" heavies responded with some Russian verbal abuse and at one stage it looked like the rival groups might tear into each other.

Fear and loathing at Lenin's tomb.

The eXile newspaper employed a handy guide that made Moscow's nocturnal delights vaguely decipherable to clueless outsiders such as myself. *Titanik*, for instance, was this hip new spot near the Young Pioneer's Stadium. *The eXile* described it thus: 'No place could better exemplify the excesses of the New Russia than *Titanik*. Bitching interior, ear-splitting techno, babe-o-litas and their flathead keepers, Die Hard security, black-eyed patrons sucking down Evians. Awesome sound system, kick-ass parties. A must see.'

In Russia, those with bulging money clips wield the power. Entrepreneurs are seizing the day, in a haphazard fashion, as if someone had allowed third world taxi drivers to set the rules of the road. And I can't emphasise strongly enough how much the sex industry seems to grease the wheels of Russian tourism. The lobbies of all hotels catering for foreigners are heaving with prostitutes, crawling with sex workers, dotted with dyevs. In Moscow discos, it's best to exercise caution with friendly blondes in thigh-high boots. Because whatever they might say to the contrary, they're out to hoover your wallet faster than they can utter 'Sure I take AmEx.' Western businessmen flock to places like *Night Flight*, a disco near the Tverskaya metro station, just north of the Bolshoi Ballet. Here it costs $50 just to get through the door, which is staunchly guarded by thick-necked Flathead bouncers. A *Stolichnaya* vodka and orange is $10. Patrons can't believe their luck as a succession of centrefold wannabes rub up against them. But these girls don't want clever conversation, even if Billy Joel is playing on the sound system. It's all strictly business.

A wide-eyed Birmingham carpet salesmen, who only just stopped short of actually drooling on his half-mast tie, filled me in on the sordid details - $300 plus cab-fare plus tip to the old lady who acts as a security guard on the floor of your hotel, who will then, provided her palm is greased, turn a blind eye to your visitor. Each transaction at *Night Flight* involving a balding, sweaty western sales rep was overseen by a flathead in a shiny suit. The Moscow Mafia is an omnivorous beast whose tentacles spread far and wide.

Whether any Lokomotiv fans would have had quite the same story to tell two weeks ago in Leeds, I'm not so sure. But then again...

My dowdy, mediocre lodgings at the Rossiya Hotel cost $150 a night and overlooked the multi-coloured cupolas and domes of St Basil's Cathedral, the Kremlin and Red Square, and the brooding expanse of the Moscow River. On my first day in the city, I made a bee-line straight for Red Square's cobble-stoned expanse. And was immediately engulfed by a number of fur-hat salesmen, who in the coming days would prove to be as persistent as athlete's foot. As far as souvenirs go, these Russian Army issue items are pretty much indispensable, so I decided to get the bargaining out of the way as early as possible. The gaunt peddler wanted to charge me $30 at first, but we soon settled on a "best, special price" of $10. There were plenty of Leeds supporters doing the same thing, and for the next few days, the best way to spot a Leeds United fan in Moscow was to look for the daft bloke in the thin, short-sleeved Leeds shirt and the silly hat.

The perishing, minus eight degree cold held no terrors, but if these geezers did need some warming up, they would head for the nearest bar to tackle the abundant varieties of local vodka. *Stolichnaya* was, predictably, the dram of choice, and there was also a growing market for a pert little number called *Pertsovka* – with its alarming picture of a pair of red chillies on the label. In fact, generous slugs of *Pertsovka* chilli vodka proved to be the ideal tipple to ward off the cold of November in Moscow. One morning I joined a smallish queue, made up mostly of white and yellow shirted Leeds fans, to gaze upon Lenin's tomb. Perhaps they were prompted to go by thoughts of the memorial statue of their own fiery little hero, Billy Bremner. I didn't ask. Twice I was searched by heavy-coated cops, before I could file past the body of "old ginger-whiskers". Hewed from marble and the colour of gravel and dried blood, the mausoleum is no longer the magnet it once was. There were only about twenty of us die-hards on a cold, drizzly Tuesday.

On the evening of the match I had dinner at *1 Red Square*, a trendy restaurant with New York City-style prices. I found the venue's culinary abilities far outstripped their English skills. The restaurant advertised a "violence duet", which consisted of a pair of traditionally-costumed violinists seducing the tourist diners with tunes from *Doctor Zhivago*. After hearing them perform, violence was, after all, the correct choice of word. I escaped to the subway and travelled twenty minutes to the 18,000 seater Lokomotiv stadium north east of the city centre.

The history of Lokomotiv Moscow football club is every bit as utilitarian and communist era as it sounds. A bunch of railway workers who enjoyed a post-work kick-around formed an organized club in 1923, four years after Leeds United began, and six years after the Bolsheviks stormed the Winter Palace in St Petersburg to kick-start the Russian Revolution. Lokomotiv had a reputation as the flatterers-to-deceive of Russian football. They would often start seasons at a gallop, before fading to a jog-trot when the going got tough.

The Lokomotiv fans were friendly and curious and some scarf-swapping took place between the rival supporters, though not all the locals seemed to understand the give-and-take aspect of this ritual – thinking they had been given a present instead. The police in the ground were wary to begin with, given Leeds' well-honed reputation for violence, but the men in blue relaxed as it became clear that, though raucous, the Leeds fans were essentially behaving themselves. I just couldn't associate myself with the loons, though, and took my seat in another stand. It was a nose-numbingly cold November night, even though I was dressed in a North Pole windbreaker suitable for Everest ascents, a thick Lokomotiv scarf and, to complete the disguise, a Russian ice hockey woollen hat that I'd found for $5 at a subway stall the previous day. As the game began, shrill bellows of "Russia! – Russia!" echoed around the Lokomotiv stadium and continued for just about the full ninety minutes. Imagine Leeds fans chanting for England! Around me were gnarled old men hunched over brown paper bags filled with peanuts; a few thousand Muscovites sputtering pink peanut shells, and the odd rope of saliva, into the frigid Moscow night.

As far as team news was concerned, I only had to glance away to the scoreboard on my left where the entire Leeds line-up was meticulously reproduced. In Cyrillic script, that is. I knew for sure that Eirik Bakke was in the line-up, because Bakke is written the same way in Cyrillic as it is in Roman script. There, the resemblances ended. The 4-1 lead for Leeds were protecting from the first leg at Elland Road meant any fears of a comeback by the local side were dispelled during the opening half. Nevertheless, Lokomotiv should have scored in the first minute, and for a while it seemed they might get the early goal that would make the tie interesting. But Leeds scored when Ian Harte rammed home a penalty in the 16th minute, after Harry Kewell's charge into the box had been rudely halted by a mistimed challenge from the appropriately named Alexei Arifoullin.

From that moment, any confidence Lokomotiv had mustered from an enthusiastic start evaporated. The Leeds fans sensed this, and a new slant on the sophisticated Leeds fan song "Stand up if you hate Man U" was swiftly composed by a couple of terrace poet laureates. "Hats off if you hate Man U!" chanted the masses, in a nod to their new items of Russian headgear, and everyone waved their $10 fur Army hats above their heads. The rusty old ground was only half full and half of those, mostly disgruntled Lokomotiv fans, failed to reappear after half-time. By the end of the game there were probably as many Leeds fans as Locomotiv ones - about a thousand each. The second-half seemed more like a friendly, although Leeds could have scored more than the two goals they managed from the injury-prone Michael Bridges. Leeds were coasting, miles ahead on aggregate and the fans took advantage of the relaxed atmosphere by lobbing cameras to the police and the limbering-up Leeds substitutes like Alan Smith to take photos of them.

Thanks to Western European TV schedules, the match didn't end till after eleven o'clock local time and it was deathly cold on the walk back to the subway. My team had survived, it was now just a question of whether I would. I warmed up with a chilli vodka or two at Armadillos, and checked out their Tex-Mex menu for a late dinner. My Cyrillic-deciphering skills must have been affected by the cold. I thought I'd ordered burritos, but ended up with a dish consisting of two sausages and a pork chop smothered in ketchup that comprised one part meat and two parts leathery sinew. A crew of loud and lewd Leeds fans barged into Armadillos as I was finishing my gristle-fest. They bellowed and chanted and launched into foul tirades about all things Russian. Of course, such rants were lost on the locals, who carried on sipping vodka in that mildly irritating, offhand way they've perfected.

It was time to move on. No more smashed, hostile Leeds fans. No more flatheads and dull-eyed babe-o-litas at gung-ho nightclubs. No laser-strewn discos. No desperate sales reps and blondes in thigh high boots. Just a quiet beer in a convivial pub. Please. So I headed for the *Arbat* where I found a small pub with old movie posters on the walls and imported beer on the menu. It was a great place to nurse a lager on my final night in Moscow.

I headed back to the Rossiya Hotel after midnight. Exiting the Kitay Gorod metro station, I was serenaded by four Tchaikovskyplaying violinists (violence quartet?), and two reed-thin teenagers tried to sell me fake DVDs. At the Rossiya, I answered 'no' to the question 'do you want sex massage?' six times and had a final beer at the bar. In the best faux Las Vegas tradition, the lobby had a sad bank of sullen one-armed bandits which blinked and tinkled 24 hours a day. I watched a Russian father sit his four pre-teen children on the four tall bar-chairs in front of the machines. Each child was given a saucerful of coins and they spent the next hour robotically feeding the slots. Papa had no doubt told his brood that in the brave new Abramovich Russia there was gold to be had in them thar machines. And in that determined Russian fashion, those kids were damned if they were going to leave without getting their share.

Since that match, the fortunes of my team rose even higher - then plummeted. Proud dreams of a brand new superstadium proved just that, dreams. Trips to Europe have become no more than fond memories. However, after Lokomotiv's ground underwent an extensive, and much-needed renovation in 2002, their fortunes on the field gathered momentum like, well, like a runaway locomotive. Lokomotiv Moscow are now a fixture in the Champions League, and won the Russian league title in both 2003 and 2004. Their ground is regarded as the premier soccer stadium in Russia, a 30,000 capacity venue with state-of-the-art facilities that are a far cry from that bleak November night when Leeds United came to town.

Soccer is not about justice. It's a drama – and criminally wrong decisions against you are part and parcel of that.

Pete Davies

Tinkler Mad

by John Dennison

Who's your father, who's your father, who's your father referee?

You ain't got one you're a bastard, you're a bastard referee.

Tinkler. Call yourself a ref? I'll call you a prat. How could you allow it, Ray?

Sheer madness and it still makes me sick.

It's over thirty years ago? So bloody what? West Brom were miles offside. What kind of ref were you? As Don Revie said, 'Tinkler ruined nine months of hard work.'

One man's diabolical decision.

Yours.

All right, Leeds were playing crap and were losing one-nil but it turned out even a draw would have been enough to win the league and stop Arsenal doing the double. Play on, play on, you waved. (You must have been bought, you swine!) And a gleeful West Brom duly did. Television replays did not suggest it was a marginal decision. They showed Colin Suggett to be offside by so far that he was embarrassed, at first, to carry on.

Miles offside were they? Yes, I would say their player was at least a million miles offside. *Nobhead.*

Only your comforting double wave and honeyed message of encouragement gave West Brom the nerve to ignore a frantically waving linesman and play on.

Go doolally? I didn't but the crowd bloody well did. I felt mad though, mad as Jack the Hat that something so obviously, bleeding clearly unfair had happened. The fans surged forward from the Kop, in near hysteria.

Did you see that? I doubt it, you were too busy dreaming of your pay out, weren't you?

Probably they were trying to get the game called off, if there was any logic at all in what they were up to. I prefer to think they were intent on no more than merely trying to rip you apart limb from limb. Limb from lousy, stringy, hen's-arsed limb. It wasn't "just like a crowd scene", an Andy Gray cliché that drives me mad incidentally, Ray, it was one. All thanks to you, *shitbag*.

Commentator Barry Davies picked up the furious spectators' feelings and sympathised with the riot. 'And Leeds will go mad! And they have every right to go mad!' was his take. I found out later who took the blame while you got off scot-free.

In the end, only a handful of diehard Leeds nutters made it on to the pitch, others being restrained by an unhealthy combination of police, stewards, reason and cowardice. Those few were dragged writhing, struggling, protesting into custody, their blood boiling. But, put another way, only five had made it. 36,807 had not. Any crimes of passion had been prevented, surely?

Wrong! At least according to our lousy "justice" system.

The game finished and Leeds lost. Eventually Leeds lost the

championship too. Leeds got fined for their unruly fans. *Are you listening Tinkler?* Leeds had their ground shut for four games the next season, dropped some points by having to play on neutral grounds, lost the next championship and their own double by a single point. You, Ray Tinkler, received your full match fee. I'd have to be crazy to suggest you received a bung from Arsenal because referees don't throw matches do they? And Arsenal managers don't deal in bungs, do they?

Some weeks later, I happened to be in court. Not for anything I'd done. Don't be daft. I was observing, as you do. Let's call it a chance visit and as chance would have it, the infamous five, instead of being treated like the winning sperms, having beaten off thousands of weaker rivals, were treated to a good dollop of British Justice.

I bet you didn't even know that did you? Nah, why should you give a toss?

How crazy their antics seemed in the cold light of a courtroom's day. Tinkler, YOU should have been in the dock. YOU should have blubbered a pathetic but unconvincing apology before being taken out on to the Headrow and given the rightful bullet.

Prathead. Wally. Scumbag. Shyster.

Instead, Leeds fans in new suits stood in shame before the beak. Defence pleaded mitigation. It was coolly rejected. The prosecutor catalogued their anti-social antics. Oh, and a further monster criminal had been added to the list. He had trampled someone's flowerbed in post-match rage.

But when rage has gone and pansies have been pulped, the Law swings into action. Fines flew around the room, felons were bound over and justice was finally seen to be done. It would be a long time before any of those criminals would attempt to invade a football pitch or trample pansies again in response to an insane decision against the team they loved by a loony ref. Thanks Ray.

I'll see you later. YOU KNOW WHERE.

<u>Contract:</u> 1. to enter into an agreement with (a person, a company etc) to do something on mutually agreed and binding terms, often in writing. 2. to make or become *smaller, shorter, narrower* etc

There's no-one more loyal at a football club than the fans – and fans don't sign contracts.

The Armchair Philosopher

Saturday with Stu

by Daniel Clark

The Channel Five late night movie has just finished. 2:30 am. Stu downs the rest of the bottle. Living room-warmed Newcastle Brown Ale. The rancid taste of dregs makes him run his tongue along the roof of his mouth.

'Big day tomorrow Stu.'

Friday night ritual almost complete. Hot shower then bed. Stu's shirt and jeans are already laid out on the ironing board down stairs. He's forty four years (seasons*) old and single. Of course he doesn't iron.

*note - Stu measures his age in seasons

The tingling of excitement has already begun in his stomach and throat.

He steps into the cloud of shower. This is the part where you might start thinking that Stu isn't like most people. Strange markings are visible through the vapour. Eleven circles in a 4-4-2 formation are spread across Stu's back. The circles have numbers inside them and a bold font text beneath them.

Once Stu has finished washing himself down in his envelope of steam spray you will get a clearer picture. You will be able to read the words beneath the numbers.

He closes his eyes as his head hits the pillow.

His mind swims with brown ale as he pictures the walk. Sun gleaming just above the old Co-Op building in the mid day haze. The swaggering army of supporters heading up the steady incline. Arms raised along with chorus voices. Kick-off is twelve hours away but he can already feel the waves of anticipation pulsing out across the city, like invisible spiritual radar topping bungalows, scaling tower blocks and penetrating basement rooms, charging the night air with anticipation and optimism.

To someone like Stu the phrase "tomorrow is a big one" is a blasphemy. Every game is a big one. Every Saturday is the big one. The one to work long hours on a weekday for. The one to blow out your girlfriend for. The one to sell your vital organs for.

Yeah you guessed it.

Football = Life.

This isn't a clever Nike advert, or a Coca Cola one for that matter. It's just Stu's life.

Make your judgements if you will. Stu doesn't care.

On a percentage basis Stu is happier with his life than most (72% happy) which means the rest of us can stop grinning about him and take notes.

Stu has been living for his Saturdays longer than he has been fantasizing about women dressed as school girls. He has sat in the same seat (East stand row L, seat 34. approx. 100 metres from ground level) between 3pm and 5pm every Saturday for the last fourteen years.

He has only not made it to that seat on two occasions in all of that time.

One time Stu missed a game was when he was in hospital. He had the misfortune to suffer two broken arms and two broken legs after failing to scale the High Level Bridge at 2am. Carrying 27 units of alcohol in his system he was attempting to plant a flag which read "We beat the Scum 2-0!" at its summit, having previously completed a 12 hour bender. Don't ask how he got to the ground the week after. It wasn't pretty.

Stu will get out of bed at 10am.

He relies on his natural body clock for this time on a Saturday, however, he needs the help of an alarm clock every other day of the week. That's something for us all to think about. So Stu will get up and go downstairs and pull the morning paper from the letter box, probably ripping the front page off as he carelessly does so. Then he will fantasise again over Saturday's page three. In Stu's head she is never naked. Her parchment skin will always be clad in the beloved shirt, sometimes the away one. Have a think, does that constitute a more or less wholesome fantasy?

After Stu is done with the paper he goes for a long shower and a shave. Air drying as he walks to the ironing board he will check his phone for messages where he will have two. They will be from Malky and Geoff.

Msg 1. **Haway the Toon!**

Msg 2. **Oh me lads wa gannin aal the way!**

After listening in on his messages you'll see his tattoo clearly:

	10	**9**	
	Asprillia	**Ferdinand**	

14	**8**	**18**	**19**
Ginola	**Beardsley**	**Lee**	**Gillespie**

3	**4**	**5**	**2**
Beresford	**Howey**	**Albert**	**Barton**

1

Hislop

Stu doesn't regret the tattoo. In fact he is proud of what it says about him. It speaks volumes for his measure of faith. Stu knew full well that the league was far from being decided. The "Newcastle United" header and "95-96 Premiership Champions" footer which grace his back at respective ends of the vertebrae are wholly inaccurate and conjure a painful memory to many of his fellow Geordies. These markings, although carrying the poison of bitterness, enable Stu to remember more clearly the feeling of being arrogant in supremacy, however premature and short lived. It's something which only after a heavy night "on the lash" he would ever admit he'd never again experience as a Newcastle fan.

The only other time Stu missed a game was when his mother was dying of cancer in hospital. It wasn't as tragic as it sounds. In fact, to the two of them it was beautiful. As fitting and natural as this kind of thing could possibly be. Stu's mother was admitted to Newcastle General Hospital on the day Newcastle played West Ham in the 95/96 season. The hospital was a stone's throw away from the ground. She had been battling the cancer for around three seasons and had told him it was time she called it a day. She lay on the bed, draped in the giant NUFC flag Stu bought her at Christmas four seasons ago. He sat holding her hand as the afternoon sun filtered through the dull windows, yellowed by NHS grime, the roars, jeers and chants of the crowd just 200 metres away. They sat silently. A communion of spirits honing in on the mass human symphony of emotions reaching crescendos a ball kick away. Newcastle beat West Ham 4-2.

Stu's mother died with a soft smile.

'Aah tewld yi Asprilla was warth the six million quid.'

Her triumphant last words.

Malky and Geoff will be meeting Stu in the pub but that's later's story. Stu can feel the adrenaline spreading through him like ice water through the veins. He only really feels like himself on a weekend. He works for the council answering phones to the sound of OAPs complaining that the kids in the street are kicking footballs against their house. He has to sound as sympathetic as possible but really he sides with the kids. He thinks old people are bitter and jealous of the energy and enthusiasm of the young. Stu still considers himself a kid. He's still up for a kick about.

There's a lot of pride at stake today. There's a rivalry surrounding this one and it's not just between the teams, it's personal. At work Stu sits opposite a Man United fan. A real one. His name is Ian. Unsurprisingly he's from Essex. Of course he's never been to Old Trafford but he remembers every occasion that Man United have beaten Newcastle, and has an excuse for any occasion Newcastle have beaten Man United. Remember the 5-0 thrashing? Albert rounds off Newcastle's best performance of the season with a delicate chip over Schmeichel from twenty five yards. According to Ian, the Reds had a bout of food poisoning from the pre-match breakfast. Yeah he's that kind of supporter. Stu can't decide who he dislikes more, the old people firing sharp decibels at his ear drums eight hours a day, or Ian.

Right now Stu is pulling on his jeans. Jeans that Stu has worn so many times that they are as much Stu as they are denim. They don't get ironed; they sit on the ironing table like a post modernist Sculpture. A clever computer-generated image of a pair of jeans occupied by an invisible man. The word "contours" springs to mind.

White socks (3 for £3) are next up. Stu's feet then glide into a pair of "Saturday Sambas" (*Adidas* product placement). He's got a different pair for each day of the week. All are leather, black and white. The hallowed piebald. They are similar in some respects to his jeans, the leather stretched around the contours of his size elevens, a leather-finish painted plaster cast of his "awld trotters".

(Subliminal mantra):

Key. Phone. Wallet. Season ticket. Pack of Tabs. Lighter.

Stu no longer has to remember these things. They have begun to remember themselves. He hasn't picked them up for years now. They just know they have to be there. Scene from Terminator 2. Liquid metal man. Broken off parts just melt back into his body as he walks past them out of the flames. Seemingly inanimate, these objects have more of a claim to be part of Stu than the scars or moles he has picked up over the last few years. We could argue for months on the philosophy of what counts as being part of a person.

Now for the final act; Flag on the summit, crown on the king. Stu reaches for the shirt.

The 0.6 seconds between Stu looking at and picking up the colours of the gods is a blink of an eye. Within that blink rests a lifetime of innate pride which produces more endorphins than feelings of spirituality. Stu isn't just a chunk of organs, muscle, vein and tendon that came from a reproductive system. Similarly this shirt isn't just a mass of fabric hammered into shape by a production line. This shirt represents one hundred and thirteen years of tribal history. A mark of established common ground, an emblem of loyalty and pride to thousands of very different people. For a hundred and thirteen years this shirt has united thousands under its illustrious symbol.

(More Adidas coming).

100% Polyester. Made in Tunisia. "The brand with three stripes".

It's large and long sleeved. Stu would never tell you but he knows at some level that on the tag at the inside bottom of the shirt, there are eight different flags. He would claim he is unsure about this but he knows. He knows this because at some point, much like the pocket fillers, the shirt became a part of him, its conscious slightly attached to his own. Hairs on his chest entwine in the fabric of the polyester once a week. The shirt becomes a part of his skin, a part of him, every week.

Germany. Japan. The United Kingdom. France. Ireland. The USA. Spain. Canada. He feels his fibres being stretched, similar to the sensation of being pegged to hang outside to dry. But different, more of an all over feeling. No stitch is left un-warped. It's less strained than the pegging too. He doesn't worry too much about it. He doesn't worry because he is used to it by now. The shirt knows that he is a big brand product designed purposely for the sport of football. Specifications like CLIMACOOL© and CLIMALITE© technology (both of which in case you were unsure, are state of the art fabrics developments) mean that he has been specially produced to cope with the strains of modern day-to-day wear. He has faith in the German scientists working like silent mad men back at headquarters. He's confident almost to the point of garmently arrogance because his underarm netted mesh means he will also be able to control perspiration and keep his insides at optimum temperature under various stress levels.

He is proud to represent a hundred and thirteen years of loyalty and tradition and he is determined to approach every public appearance in parade mentality. He idolises the stamina of the Crucifix, he is inspired by the weight of importance the Star of David carries.

A double tap on the framed crest crowning the wall of Stu's hallway, two seahorses either side of a black and white shield. Superstition once a week is spiritual. While Stu is communing with his shirt the organic parts of him are walking out of the front door and getting in a taxi.

L554 LRB

Stu gets picked up by the same taxi driver each week. Each week Stu holds superficial conversations with Paul Sanders, Licence No. 1237 GG#1. Stu never remembers the conversations. Saturday at 1:30pm has its own consciousness. It doesn't belong to Stu. Like a rogue folder kept on a Microsoft desktop.

C:\Documents and Settings\Stu\Desktop\taxidriver.

It was put there by the taxi driver. Word documents on his wife, spreadsheets of his medical history, PowerPoint® presentations of hobbies and interests. There's even a miscellaneous sub file full of his interesting stories and hilarious anecdotes. So while Stu's Microsoft Xp® debugged program converses with the taxi driver Stu can meditate over the coming fixture. His mind is sending and receiving 6,324 bits of information per second every Saturday for ten minutes that he knows nothing about. He has the latest Norton

Antivirus© protector. He's firewalled, safe from the unwanted intrusions being cascaded by Paul the taxi driver.

Disconnecting from server please wait…

Little egg timers are flipping before Stu's eyes as he leaves the taxi and enters The Fog of Smoke, commonly known as The Three Bulls' Heads. Stu is only five minutes walk from the ground now. He hears the two square miles of concrete and stainless steel projecting a silent greeting as he enters the pub. The ground knows a lot about Stu, he communes with it every other Saturday, his thoughts pulsing up into its rafters. The stadium knows what's at stake today. It's heard all about Ian. The stadium knows that Ian has a ticket for the match too. He'll be sitting in the Sir John Hall Stand (level 7, row S, seat 362; a whopping 14 flights of stairs from the ground floor). The stadium knows he will be there wrapped smugly in a heavy wool coat to conceal his Man United shirt. Stu dislikes Ian because he is a prick. The stadium dislikes Ian because he represents a safety hazard on the terraces. The silent figure of Ian will be enveloped by thousands of drunken Geordies. There is only one policeman to every 12,643 supporters at each Newcastle home game.

Malky and Geoff are at the east corner of the bar at a 45 degree angle from the door. They don't realise it, but they have subconsciously picked a spot in the bar that mirrors where the three of them sit together in the stadium (East stand row L, seat 34. approx. 100 metres from ground level remember!). The rectangular bar doubles for the consecrated turf. Pictures of dogs playing pool become corporate billboards. This is the same place they stand in every Saturday (surprise surprise).

Two bottles of Brown Ale and a pint of *Guinness*. The Undying Round. The three of them have got the round in an astonishing 1560 times between them. There's a formula for brain cell destruction here. Average games per season times the number of seasons being season ticket holders times the number of pints per pre-match warm up 20x26x3 = 1560 rounds. Then you times that by the number of pints bought per round, meaning they have bought and consumed 4680 pints between them.

Shame you don't get loyalty points in pubs (or maybe a good thing).

The Guinness is for Geoff. His taste buds would prefer the new Guinness Extra Cold. Geoff suspects as much but won't allow it. He has been drinking Guinness for twenty six seasons in this bar. Compulsive and stubborn are common characteristics amongst football supporters.

The hour long warm up in The Three Bulls' Heads passes strangely. When people like this spend twenty six seasons talking about the same subject (Newcastle United) they begin to evolve an extrasensory way of communicating. Again it falls to mathematics. This time statistics – "Probability".

Deep breath, here it goes.

Each of the three men have become attuned to the others' personality so much that they each know how the other will react to a certain event. They have memorised the idiosyncrasies of speech in each other member of the drinking group, so they each know how the other will put their opinion across. Finally because they share this same space every week of the season they can judge precisely at what point each of the others will speak their mind. As a result, through the process of probability perfected over twenty six seasons, each knows exactly what the other is thinking, how and when he is thinking about it, the average time it will take them to articulate the opinion in their heads, at what point it will be expressed into speech, and at what speed and manner it will be spoken.

Scary isn't it? You can tell because it's a long sentence. The end product of this is that when they each congregate at the pub they stand in silence. Each performing the same conversation in their heads, reciting the exact replica of the other's imagined discussion. Precise mathematical silence. Honest.

The point at which the three of them break this natural/unnatural silence is at 2:45pm (Greenwich Meantime). The five minute walk to the ground. It's at this point that we lose Stu completely. That's because the essence of Stu's being is now tapped into that of the 52,000 other fans making their way up the steady incline (12 degrees in most places) leading up to the ground. It really is a flurry of spiritual soaring on Stu's behalf. His consciousness is splintered into thousands of elated little shards. At one with the rippling barcode that is making its way towards the ground.

The security camera that records the mass parade of contrasting shade on the corner of the old Co-Op building is carrying a bit of Stu as well. There is a part of Stu's brain that acknowledges its presence every time he makes this walk. The existence of the camera is imprinted into his mind the way his presence is being video-recorded into the camera's digital archive. This mutual acknowledgement of subsistence means that it qualifies to blend with one of those little shards of Stu. Regardless of what you might think, the camera has its own form of consciousness. Seeing in pixels, learning more and more about the world each day of recording into its electronically maturing memory banks. It can speak fluent Geordie, disjointed English and a splattering of Chinese Mandarin. Considering this blend of language and the electronic monotone of its expression, the security camera's own accent is understandably strange.

When it was first commissioned the then young Stu-Cam's days were filled with wonder. Spying life excitedly through vivid colours. An age of serial numbered days spent constantly asking questions of the hub of activity being viewed through a shiny crisp lens. Over time these questions were answered.

Stu-Cam has witnessed much in his electronic lifetime. He's been observer to crime, generosity and love both lost and found; a kaleidoscope of human endeavour and emotion. Over the years he has matured into what can only be described as the David Attenborough of the security systems world. He is a wizened old expert of the human condition. Stu-Cam carries more than enough credentials to take over Jerry Springer's television slot.

These days Stu-Cam undertakes his job in Securor-Systems with a meticulous vigour. Faces, names, times, appearances, movements, possible destinations and camera community interlinks all deftly catalogued in nanoseconds. Stu-Cam has been on the block a long time. He knows the need for security is great and that accuracy is crucial. Stu-Cam knows that at 2:52pm Stu will pass into and out of his sight heading in a north easterly direction en route to St. James Park. Stu-Cam is able to make the informed guess that Stu will arrive at his seat at around 2:58pm. The stands are now full. Anticipation sends waves of nausea and tension rippling through the thousands gathered within the ground. The gathering of so many people, so many hopes, fears and dreams produces an unforgettable energy. This is where football is more than just a game. This is where football becomes life.

52,000 people have now become joined in one consciousness. Stu is part of that consciousness. He's standing arms raised to the rafters, adding his own vocal focus to the roar that ripples out from the east stand and flows around the stadium. A rising tide becoming denser, more aggressive and more overpowering as it circles the pitch. Twenty two men are spread across the turf. For the next 90 minutes these men are the most important on the planet; men chosen to grace the grass because of their exceptional talents; their ability to manipulate a football bringing with it the opportunity to shape the joy of the future and erase the pain of the past.

Man United kick off the occasion, accompanied by a second wave of sound; the optimistic roar of the Toon Army. The noise dies as the ball skids across the pitch. The away players begin to get a feel for the ball, the pitch and the occasion. Stu begins his meditation. Eruptions of sound echo around the stadium. Newcastle make two tackles and manage to string together two passes before a badly timed offside trap allows Ruud Van Nistelrooy to race onto a Gary Neville long ball. Stu hasn't even sat down yet.

Newcastle 0 – 1 Man United.

Although Stu is sitting almost a quarter of a mile left of his colleague from work, he can hear Ian's jeers. They lance into Stu like rancid barbs to the heart. The thought of Ian's scrunched up face and smug demeanour is making thoughts of Monday unbearable. It's worse than losing a job, worse than losing a limb. Please God. Please take a limb instead!

The expletives from the Toon Army faithful almost drown out the celebrations of the small contingent of Man United supporters. Almost.

The teams reform to restart the match. The Toons lift their heads from their hands. The soldiers in black and white restart to the chorus of devoted followers, all chanting in unison:

OH ME LADS! Y' SHUD I SEEN IS GANNIN! GAN' ALAANG T' SCOTSWAAAD RUUED JUUST T' SEE WHATS HAPPNIN! AAAL THE LADS 'N LASSES THERE, AAAL THE SMILIN' FACES, GAN' ALAANG T' SCOTSWAAAD RUUED!! T' SEE THE BLAYDON RACES!!

The breakfast of champions

isn't cereal

it's

the

opposition

Nick Seitz

Reds Under The Table

by Paul Hatt

I'll tell you what doolally is.

Think of a Wednesday night in May.

A semi-detached house in Outwood, West Yorkshire.

Three forty something blokes sat in front of a widescreen TV, each with a beer in hand anticipating the start of the 2004/05 European Cup Final. Yes, The European Cup Final – not the PR friendly, re-branded title of "Champions League" Final for these old codgers. *The European Cup Final.*

The two blokes with me are Aussies, Taz the Crystal Palace fan and Dan, who supports Leeds United. Me, I'm a Londoner - a Fulham exile from the banks of the Thames. None of us have any allegiance to Liverpool or Milan, but we're looking forward to the match just the same.

Our pre-match banter at first is not about football but instead is centred on the cricket injuries we are all currently suffering with, and the wicket of three empty cans on the coffee table.

Our focus switches as the teams come out. We strike up bets as to the final score. Our hearts want Liverpool to try and make a match of it, but our heads all turn to AC Milan with the margins offered 1-0, 2-0 and 2-1.

Three more ice-cold tinnies are collected from the fridge just in time for kick-off, and with the first release of the fresh cans, so

Maldini opens the scoring. We all nod wisely, each of us stating our case as to why his pre-match prediction is still on course. Only one can per man and we're talking bollocks already.

'That's it,' pipes up Taz, 'eighty nine minutes of Italian control to come.'

'Nah,' drools the Leeds Antipodean, 'Liverpool to get one just before half-time and then AC to get the winner at the start of the second half.'

The Fulhamite mock-chokes on his beer and splutters, 'What do you Aussies know about football? Milan'll sit back and take everything Liverpool throw at them, and get a second on the counter in the final minutes of the game.'

Staring at the screen the Aussies calmly drain their tinnies. The wicket is now a pyramid.

I continue my Aussie-bashing between sips, and Dan joins in, slating the presence of Harry Kewell in the starting line-up. The lame Australian limps off after about twenty minutes. Dan leans round the pyramid and wags two fingers at the screen.

As the half continues, so the free flowing visits to the fridge are mirrored by the smooth flow of the Milan attacks. Two more Milan goals hit the back of the net, six more cans of *Castlemaine* hit the back of the neck.

By half time, the pyramid is too high to see over so Taz scrunches up his latest empty and clean bowls it. The Liverpool players had seemingly collapsed as easily.

Rather than slate Liverpool, the talk on the sofa is whether to turn over and watch some Aussie Rules. It is only a passing thought and soon we three pay our respects to the Milan dominance. Strangely there is no talk of the pre-match score predictions, all now well and truly blown out of the water. However, Harry Kewell comes in for more stick with Dan suggesting that Mr K was no doubt already on a plane out of Turkey in search of his next pay day.

With the Liverpool boss frantically searching for inspiration, so the sofa three battled with their own conundrum. In cricket there is the very complicated Duckworth Lewis calculation for rain affected games. For armchair football fans there is The Three Bs – Beer, Bladder and Bogs. It clearly states that during the first half of viewing a game no matter how many beers are consumed no toilet breaks are required. However, once half time is reached and a first trip to the bogs is made the second half becomes a procession as bladder capacity is exceeded.

After visits to "point Percy at the porcelain" as Taz puts it, then, more importantly, to the fridge, we are ready to endure the second half. All quiet until the 54th minute and then the first Liverpool goal. Gerrard's header. All three leap off the sofa, cries of 'C'mon!' bounce off the walls. As the Italians retreat, so we edge forward on the sofa.

A minute later BANG…a speculative shot from Smicer somehow eludes the keeper. Game-on.

We can't believe what we see, and on the hour don't know whether to stand or sit as a penalty is awarded to Liverpool. This calls for a drink or three.

There is anguish then ecstasy in a nano-second as the ball is stopped, then is immediately swept into the net.

6 minutes of football madness, and there are three grown men dancing around like the most ardent of Liverpool fans. And three bursting bladders are bouncing and sloshing about as the penalty shoot-out comes to its unbelievable climax.

Doolally – totally.

How? Why?

The answer's in the cans.

Confessions of a Serial Jinxer

by Russell Pearce

> "It's no longer an 11-man game."
>
> Kevin Keegan

I am going to Elland Road tomorrow to watch Leeds United. If they knew my history they'd certainly bar me. Whilst footballing pundits have expended considerable time and energy trying to determine who or what is to blame for the difficulties besetting LUFC, I can tell you now: it is all down to me.

You may feel that I am overstating my part in Leeds' fortunes. When I have put the evidence before you, you will have to agree that I am the kiss of death to sporting hopes. I should come clean straight away and admit that I am actually a Man City supporter. Now there is a club that bears testament to my destructive powers.

To continue, as it were, at the beginning; like most lads, and many lasses, my interest in football goes back to my formative years, which were spent in Switzerland. In these early days my unwitting ability to jinx a match had shown no signs. I was just a normal fan. I cut my teeth on Servette FC of Geneva in the late 60s/early 70s, when Servette was one of Switzerland's most successful clubs. Although Switzerland is not particularly renowned for its prowess on the field (matches were somewhat akin to the UK Sunday League) Servette was still a pretty mean achiever. Lured by the glitter of success my mates and I would hang around the tunnel hoping to engage star player and fellow Brit Martin Chivers in lively banter about his glory days with Spurs – though we were singularly unsuccessful in this.

One of my earliest footballing memories is of watching Servette beat the mighty Merseysiders 2-0, although I now suspect that Liverpool did not pick their top men for the job. Nevertheless, the win was a high point in Servette's story and was celebrated with much abandon, or as much abandon as a gaggle of international bankers can muster.

Aged eleven I was sent to boarding school in England. Feeling lost and far from home, my main aim was to be accepted. 'So, who do you support?' was one of the first questions I was asked on touching British soil. The proud response 'Servette,' didn't do the trick. Just blank stares and a blunt 'Who the **** are Serviette??!' Having said this, my choice of sporting heroes could have been worse. Switzerland surely has some of the strangest team names; Grasshoppers and Xamax being just two. But that's nothing: my school days would have been blighted forever had we lived in Berne.

Question, 'Who do you support then?'

Answer, 'I quite like Young Boys actually.'

(BSC Young Boys of Berne. 11 times Swiss Champions. Since 1925 they have played at The Wankdorf Stadium, now rebuilt for Euro 2008 and, sadly, renamed Stade de Suisse.)

I took a mental step back, a shuffle forward and decided to realign my allegiances. I reviewed my options. I was living in Worcester. Worcester City could not be called top flight by even their most committed fans. Aston Villa? No, didn't like the shirt. This also ruled out West Ham. As you can see, my decisions were based on sound research and clear empirical evidence. I asked around and found that there was just one First Division club that no one else in the school supported. So it was that my choice came to rest on Manchester City, a team that soon started to reel under the impact of such a momentous decision.

At this stage I still appeared to be just a normal schoolboy fan, but gradually "The Jinx" started to sharpen its claws. When I began supporting Man. City in 1970 they were riding high, propelled on a froth of achievement that had peaked with their championship and FA Cup wins in 68 and 70; and that's where it stopped, apart from a brief return to form with a League Cup win in 76. In the years since that historic victory they have struggled on, sometimes in divisions so low that at most away games the ever loyal City supporters have outnumbered the home crowd by around three to one.

My education in UK footballing mores advanced slowly. The biggest stumbling block to my enjoyment of the beautiful game was Mr Wheeler, a formidable creature and my housemaster. Boarders were allowed into town (about 500 yards away) on Saturday afternoons, but getting to Manchester was out of the question. Even the nearer grounds required maximum subterfuge. Hence, on one occasion, a coach load of Wolves fans was treated to the bemusing sight of two grubby school kids ducking out of sight as we pulled past the school. A trip into town to stock up on pencils could hardly account for our presence on the Football Special.

The Midland Red Football Special was my passport to sporting bliss. For a very small sum the Special would take you to a random location. It didn't matter where: it could be St Andrews, Molineux or Villa Park, it was simply enough to breathe in the heady excitement of the game. After pulling up somewhere near the ground, the routine would always be the same. The driver would stand, face the fifty or so intrepid supporters and announce, 'Roight you lot. Oi'll be here for 20 minutes after the final whistle, after that yam walkin' 'ome!' – and he meant it.

These attendances at various West Midlands clubs were not regular enough to forge any particular allegiance and so they largely escaped The Jinx. Leeds was not so lucky.

It was when Dave (my best mate at school) and I teamed up that the problems for LUFC really began. Being from Yorkshire, Dave was already a Leeds fan. So, throughout the golden era of the early 70s they suffered at my hands probably as much as Man. City.

Those of us old enough to remember what a dominant force LUFC was during the Revie years might be surprised to examine the statistics and see how little silverware they won at that time. True fans know all about Jim Montgomery's save and Ray Tinkler's dodgy offside decision; now it is time for them to understand The Jinx and its part in Leeds' downfall.

The Jinx is capricious in its nature. My first Leeds game was an FA Cup away fixture at Cardiff City. As Dave was a non-boarder his dad was the lucky person chosen to escort us to the match. That morning he left the house with solemn promises to his wife (Dave's mum) that he would take good care of his two charges.

The train snaked into Cardiff and we alighted to a station swarming with activity; but where were the fleets of buses taking the fans to Ninian Park? All the buses that we could see were heading off to various estates piled high with families and shopping. Try as we might we could see no sign of the scarf clad faithful. Having spent some time wandering, we spotted the top of a stand rising above the grey tiles – unmistakable. We hastened towards the stadium.

'Excuse me. Is this Ninian Park?'

The passer by that I had stopped regarded me with extreme disfavour, rather in the manner of someone offered a sea-slug sandwich.

'That boyo is the National Stadium. RUGBY, not bloody football!'

Somewhat discountenanced we mumbled our apologies and made good our escape around the nearest corner. Finally we found the ground and, on this occasion, The Jinx did not strike. Leeds won 2-0.

At the close of the game we decided to try for Gary Sprake's autograph. Not the best idea, he would probably have dropped the pen. With Gary in sight we belted out of the terraces and were about three yards onto the pitch before being intercepted by a burly policeman who gently invited us to move along, 'You two, xxxx off!!' We decided to comply.

That evening, back in Worcester, we assured Dave's mum that a great day had been had by all. Of course no mention was made of the pitch invasion as we settled back to watch the game on *Match of the Day*. The final whistle went, followed by a lovely close-up of two suspiciously familiar faces being ushered off the pitch. Time to make a quick exit, leaving Dave's dad to face the music.

For Leeds it was downhill all the way from here. You could be sure that if I went to a key game they were bound to lose. In 1974 they set out to bring home the FA Cup, having been thwarted by Jim Montgomery in 73 (I wasn't there... but then again, I did watch it on telly). In the fifth round Leeds were drawn against lowly Bristol City and we travelled down to Ashton Gate to witness the walkover. Before kick-off we were treated to the usual pre-match entertainment. Red-and-white-clad figures rushed at each other in a distant stand, followed by a snaking black line gradually pushing the two colours apart. More memorable though was the parachute jump, organised by a local group. The winner would be the one who landed closest to the centre circle. It was certainly unforgettable. Not one of the hapless parachutists made it into the ground, never mind the circle. They must have heard I was at the game. I have an enduring memory of some poor soul narrowly avoiding being suspended from the back of a stand. Still, he would have made an unusual mascot.

Thanks to my supportive presence Leeds had no chance and only managed a 1-1 draw. Worse still for the Whites, the replay was arranged for the following Tuesday. This being half term I was able to go up to Elland Road and finish off the job.

We arrived early for a daytime kick-off, dictated by the power restrictions of the three day week, and hung around the car park to get autographs; can kids still do that or are today's prima donnas too precious? I remember that Bremner, Hunter, Lorimer and Gray were quite amenable to scrawling a signature – little did they know with whom they were dealing. Once again The Jinx struck and hot favourites Leeds were beaten 1-0.

Dejected we made our way back to the station and boarded the Worcester train, ultimate destination – Bristol. The platform and the train next to us, the Bristol Football Special, were jammed solid. There must have been several hundred victorious Bristol City Fans and we, in our Leeds scarves (mine borrowed from Dave to help me fit in), were the sole focus of their attention. At some point they decided that it would be a fine idea to take the bulbs out of the light fittings and lob them at our train. It was rather like being a coconut on a surreal fairground. We rallied to the situation, bravely flicking the Vs from behind glass as the train pulled out to their rousing chorus of, 'See you in Bristol!'

We got off at Worcester, some 50 miles short of Bristol. I must admit that in idle moments I still delight in the thought of the thwarted Bristol City fans milling around Temple Meads waiting to begin the "second half". It's a nice thought. Not being in the intellectual Premier League it would have occurred to them only gradually that we intended to decline the invite. They would certainly have had a long wait: we stopped at least a dozen times on the stretch of line between Leeds and Wakefield, something to do with tired and emotional fans using the communication cord to hold themselves upright. I have never lurched and staggered along so slowly on any other journey, and that includes some Virgin Cross Country trips. Twenty years later, when I moved to Yorkshire, I was amazed to find that Wakefield is only just south of Leeds and not, as I had thought, almost in Birmingham.

My next trick at LUFC's expense was the Stoke City debacle. All that Leeds had to do was win this game to beat the longest undefeated run in the First Division. Had they been in the know they would have kept me away and probably held the record until Arsenal's recent triumph.

Things started well, with Leeds going 2-0 up fairly early in the game. From what I remember, each time a goal was scored a scantily-clad girl had to parade around the ground with a board showing the time of the goal. It is not difficult to imagine the reaction of a typical 70s mostly male football crowd to this, and it was compounded by the fact that the goals were going in thick and fast. At one point the poor girl wasn't even getting a rest: every time she passed go she collected another number and set off again.

Of course Stoke City staged a comeback and Leeds' hopes of a record were dashed when they lost 3-2. Dave's dad, who was once again acting as minder and chauffeur, offered us a commiserative cup of tea at the Moat House before we hit the motorway. As we entered we realized that the Leeds squad was checking out, surely a heaven sent opportunity for autographs. One look at the combined expressions decided us; we'd pass this one up.

In 1974 I went to live in France, just in time for my malign influence not to prevent Leeds winning the 74 Championship. They were not so lucky when, shortly after their 92 League title, I landed a job not 15 miles from the city. From that moment on their fate was sealed. Here I was, surrounded by Leeds supporters and, what's more, teaching in a school attended by the legendary Eddie Gray's kids. The rot set in. I didn't even have to attend a game: just driving regularly past Elland Road on my way to the M621 was enough. By now The Jinx was really motoring: rear-misses in Europe, financial chaos, court cases, Venables and eventual relegation.

Meanwhile I switched my attention back to my 'real' team, Manchester City who immediately began heading down the League faster than a greased roller skate. City supporters became an object of ridicule. I saw a play where, on being brought before the devil, a City fan is let off on the grounds that he has suffered enough already, but my sense of humour was pretty much exhausted by this time.

Even recently, it looked as though City would, with the new City of Manchester Stadium, have a second division ground so large that it could hold the entire season's visiting supporters simultaneously, but then things began to pick up for them. As City recovered to a more respectable position, I began to wonder if The Jinx was finally wearing off. Perhaps it would be safe for me to venture near a ground again. All hopes were, however, dashed for good when I returned to Switzerland earlier this year.

'How are Servette doing?' I asked a Swiss friend.

'Amateur league.'

This was seriously bad news; Servette have been Swiss champions 17 times, as late as 1999 – how could they have plunged so low? It turned out that the club had gone bust, the chairman had been imprisoned, the team relegated on the orders of a judge and the spanking new 30,000 seater stadium reduced to crowds of a few hundred watching a side of amateurs, the first team having rightly decided that playing for other clubs would give them a significant financial advantage: i.e. they would get paid.

So, I guess that The Jinx is still as strong as ever (anyone doubting the continuing power of The Jinx, take note – the last time I went to see Man. City they lost to non-league Harrogate Town - it was only a pre-season friendly but it still counts!) which gives me an idea. Since I am clearly not able to shake it, surely it's high time I put this unique talent to good use. Across the country there are millions of genuine football fans who hate the monolithic money machine that is Man. Utd. If each of you were to send me a small sum, say ten or twenty pounds, I could be persuaded to shift my allegiance to Old Trafford. A noble sacrifice on my part and, I am sure you will agree, a worthwhile investment on yours.

It's time to make Man. Utd history.

Epilogue

by Fr. Ted O'Dougal

"It's good to hate Man U" as one of my parishioners has said.

But is it?

Can I ask you, is it *really?*

As a man of the cloth I have to keep an open mind, consider other options and possibilities. I happen to know from my pastoral work in the city of Leeds that there are fans who prefer to hate Liverpool, for being too good for too long; or Everton, for being too dull for too long; or Arsenal, for being too lucky for too long (the fact that they seem to have deserved their recent successes doesn't even begin to make up for this, in fact it makes it worse I find). All fans have their own favourite teams to hate. In this sense, it can be said that Leeds fans don't stand together.

One of the favourite teams to hate in Leeds is Newcastle United, rather surprisingly you might feel, given that they've been bridesmaids more often and consistently even than Leeds. Well, I have a confession I must make – they are my favourite also. I'll tell you why. Before I saw the light and began to serve God's crew, I was a member of a very different kind of crew, in the early 90s. I can tell you, they were feckful those Geordie feckers. Took a couple of hellish beatings off them I'll tell you. Hated them ever since.

Of course, a central tenet of the faith I serve is forgiveness. Now I do understand that forgiveness can be a very difficult thing to give, so, I shall tell you a little story in the hope that it will provide some spiritual food for thought.

A little while ago, a young man living in Leeds, a student, came to me for advice about his doolally friend. This friend was head-spinningly heart-wrenchingly gut-churningly ball-breakingly toe-curlingly mad about football, and the young man was rather worried for him. As he began to tell his story I assumed that he and his pal were both fans of Leeds United, as one would I suppose, ministering as I do in such a football-doolally city. Then, suddenly, he starts up with *"Haway the Toon! Oh me lads we're gannin aal the way!"* I can tell you, my head span, my heart wrenched, my guts churned, my toes curled. Seriously, my balls nearly broke!

The young man had got me interested in a moving story of football madness and obsession, then sledge-hammered me with the hated Geordy-Pordy! We are all but flesh and my flesh was crawling (perhaps the fact he had a Geordie accent should have prepared me for this, but I happen to know there are many fans of Leeds United who have Geordie accents, as there are many Newcastle fans who have Yorkshire accents).

As the young man continued, blissfully unaware of the hatred boiling up within me, I began to realise that he was telling a story about Love. A Love so strong it sends you doolally. Love for football. Then I realised that if you merely replace the names, the dates, the places, and substitute the colours with your own, the story he was telling could have been about anyone. His experience could have been my experience. Our experience.

She had been battling the cancer for around three seasons and had told him it was time she called it a

day. She lay on her bed, draped in the giant LUFC
flag he bought her at Christmas four seasons ago. He
sat holding her hand, the roars, jeers and chants of the
crowd just a few hundred metres away. They sat
silently, a communion of spirits honing in on the mass
human symphony of emotions reaching crescendos
just a ball kick away. Leeds beat Liverpool 4-3.

> *His mother died with a soft smile.*
> *'I towd yer Viduka wer worth 'six million quid.'*
> *Her triumphant last words.*

I had to remind myself that the lad had come to me in good faith seeking guidance. So I counselled him. I advised him that it is good to have such a love for something. That the love of his crazy friend for football is something to embrace. And that recognising yourself in others is the first step to forgiveness.

This last part confused him somewhat, being as it was for my benefit, not his. Could I recognise myself in those Geordie feckers? Of course I could, I was giving it all my feck to hand out beatings to them. A thought occurred to me that making them my favourite team to hate was honouring them in some kind of way, and that I would have liked the same honour from them. Not the kind of honour a man of peace should aspire to though.

No, I aspire to be like those two Aussies and the Londoner, men with divided loyalties, yet friends. Three men who cast their devils (Red or otherwise) aside, and took joy in the passion and drama of the Champions League final. Men who found that the sheer beauty and poetry of football sent them doolally, at a time when they might have least expected it. Doolally isn't a military madhouse in India, nor is it as you might imagine some quirky little village in Ireland. It's a place we all go to sometimes. A place where we do crazy things like turn our hatred for a team and its supporters into a joy we share together. Football can take you there.

As our friend Ardal says, football is a thing of beauty and a force for good, when it's played properly. Might we not say the same of supporting it properly?

Ok, sermon over. Forgive me, sermonising is an occupational hazard in my vocation. I confessed all the above to the rather bemused young man. He responded by asking me an intriguing question. He asked, 'If you have to love everyone, then how can you support one team?' Quite a theological challenge this one. This is what I told him. Everybody needs a team to be part of. Just remember we're all playing in the same league. Without other teams there can be no leagues. Defeat the opposition if you must, but don't destroy them, or question their right to exist. Dazzle them with the brilliance of your play, your determination, the love and passion of your fans. Catch their breath, but don't stop it. I see it like this, (though it's an unofficial position I must stress): for me, supporting my team is like supporting my church, and supporting the game of football itself is like supporting God. The young lad seemed to quite like that.

May your gods go with you, and win you a trophy from time to time.

PDG Books – www.pdgbooks.com

As publishers of quality books, we have three main aims. Firstly, PDG Books is committed to promoting writing in any genre or style which is distinctive, thought-provoking and readable. Work which interests us is situated between the extremes of "literary" and "populist" so if your preference, as a reader or as a writer, is for books which are a pleasure to read but have hidden depths then our titles will be of interest to you. Secondly, PDG Books is committed to a wide range of voices, visions and points of view. We value but don't insist on writing being "cool" or "cutting edge" and we don't reject good work just because the values it promotes have been around for a long time. This means that for many people PDG Books represents a rare opportunity to write and to read the kinds of books you like best. Thirdly, PDG Books is committed to a co-operative and proactive approach to both producing and selling books. If you are a writer with an idea that we wish to take forward we will, if needed, work with you to develop your writing to a publishable quality. If you are a reader we will take great interest in your tastes and opinions and will listen to and act upon any criticisms or recommendations you send to us.